IN SEARCH OF

ISAAC GULLIVER

Legendary Dorset Smuggler

M V Angel

Wild Geese Publishing

First published 2008

Wild Geese Publishing,
3 Bridle Close, Upton,
Poole, Dorset, BH16 5SU.

Copyright 2008 Malcolm Angel

ISBN 978 0 9560715 0 7

Printed and bound in Great Britain by
Ashford Colour Press Ltd, Gosport, Hants.

Facts, legends and myths that haunt the romantic name of Isaac Gulliver are collected here. They are woven together with a descriptive narrative, based on the happenings of the day. Much held within these passages tells of very real events, and although Isaac Gulliver - due to the very nature and secrecy of his trade - cannot with any certainty at all times be linked, he is placed full square, as the brilliant general in command of his private army of White Wigs, at the centre of events throughout.

Enclosed in Poverty

From the latter half of the eighteenth century, until the year of his death in 1822, Isaac Gulliver rose to become the most notorious and successful smuggler on the south coast of England. A figure of legend and mystery and a hero of romance, Gulliver and his army of moonrakers harried the Kings preventative officers along the coast of Hampshire and Dorset, from Christchurch in the east to Lyme Regis in the west.

The smuggling of goods from across the channel was at its peak in this period, and Dorset's coastline, with its wooded creeks around the Bournemouth area and wide sweeps of deserted shingle and sand further west, made it ideal for clandestine moonlit landings. Behind the beachheads, running for many miles inland, the broad wild sweep of Dorset heathland - some of which is still visible today - was the smugglers route to the towns, hamlets, farms and coach-houses within.

Stories tell of entire communities supplementing their meagre farm wages with earnings from the illegal contraband trade. Cheating the taxman was seen as fair game, after all most of the monies collected went purely to finance a succession of foreign wars, and the Dorset agricultural worker - kept poor by wealthy landowners - had their own war to fight. For the peasant it was a constant struggle against disease and malnutrition.

It was during Gulliver's time that the Dorset labourer became 'enclosed in poverty' when, in 1770, the rural landscape of the English countryside began to change forever. From this date, and into the next decade, the landowners - greedy for even greater wealth - proceeded to annex vast acreages of land.

After these land 'enclosures' the peasants no longer had the commons on which to graze their sheep or single cow for milking, even their plots to grow vegetables had been taken from them. As a result the peasant's basic diet became one of potatoes and bread, leaving them with a mean and undernourished existence.

Smugglers were revered in such society, their trade in cut price black market goods, payment for handling, and employment in their gangs, made the difference to many lives, and in so doing bought them fame and, above all, great loyalty.

Although Gulliver's business was carried out mainly in Dorset, he was, by all accounts, a Wiltshire man, as his birth is recorded as being on the 5th of September 1745, followed by his baptism on the 29th day of the same month, in the small medieval Church of St George, in the village of Semington near Trowbridge. Local historians believe his home to have been in the area of Littlemarsh, a cluster of cottages in the southwest corner of the village.

Isaac Gulliver was born to *"Isaac Gulifor and Elizabeth his wife"*, of whom little is known. Legend and popular folklore tend to blur the facts in this period of Gulliver's early life. Uncorroborated tales tell of the boy learning the family's sideline of smuggling from his father, but the truth is that only one confusing report has come to light during his early years.

It was in the year of 1758, when Isaac could have been no more than 14 years of age, that the Salisbury Journal put the name 'Isaac Gulliver' in print. The owner of the name was reported as being one of two people against whom information was laid in connection with a fight with customs officers. Legend would have it that this report was referring to the young Gulliver. But if, as seems more likely, the allegation referred to his father then it would bear out the stories that Isaac senior was indeed involved in contraband, and that Isaac junior therefore could well have been apprenticed to his fathers trade.

The incident referred to in the Journal took place in March 1758, after four customs officers came across a cargo of tea and spirits at the foot of Bitman's Chine - now Canford Cliffs Chine.

The illicit goods were being guarded by a handful of smugglers when the revenue men apprehended them. Three officers seized the goods whilst their colleague went to fetch a cart to transport the cargo. Whilst he was away however the smugglers were greatly reinforced, apparently by 'country people', and the customs officers beaten and bound. The goods were carried off, and although officers were sent in pursuit, they were unsuccessful.

There was a new 'collector' in Poole at this time and he appraised his board of this event, stating in his report that he should have gone himself if it had not been for the height of the plantation work and a sale at the Customs House.

Some attempt was made however to try to bring the smugglers to justice, and a reward of £20 - a considerable sum in those days - was offered for information. The notice published in the Salisbury Journal on the 24th April 1758, reads:

Whereas on the 23rd day of March last, about seven o'clock in the morning, Ormond Matthews, Peter Shank, and John Robbins Officers of the Customs in the Port of Poole, were assaulted and beat by a large gang of Smugglers unknown, on the North shore between Poole and Chistchurch: Who also rescued and carried off a large quantity of Tea the said officers had seized, and had then in their possession: The Honorable Commissioners of His majesty's Customs, are pleased to promise a reward of Twenty Pounds, to be paid upon conviction of each of the persons concern'd in the said Offence.

This prompted an attempt to secure the money by one Robert Wilkins. But his affidavit accusing *'Mark Chamberlain and Isaac Gulliver, very often at the New Inn within the Parish of Downton'* of involvement in the crime came to nothing.

Most likely, when the officers called on the two men, there would have been a dozen witnesses to vouch for them being nowhere near the scene of the crime. As for Robert Wilkins, his statement would no doubt have made him a very unpopular man, and one can only speculate on his fate.

Regardless however of whether the father taught the boy the moonraker trade or not, it is known that he had his doubts about his sons legitimacy. He made this abundantly clear, when, in drawing up his last will and testament in 1765, he referred to his wife's offspring as *"My son or reputed son Isaac Gulliver, otherwise Matravers"*. It was in the same year that he passed away.

His headstone, which stands miraculously preserved, a few feet from the western gable of St George's Church, has a line carved in the stone, subdividing the face vertically in two; on the left it reads:

In
Memory Of
Isaac Gulliver
Died Nov ye 29 1765
Aged 52 Years.

Then, on the right hand side of the of the central line it reads:

Also
In Memory Of
Love The Wife Of
Jacob Gulliver
Who Died June ye 24th 1779
Aged 55 Years

Likewise Mary
The Daughter Died
Dec 16th 1781
Aged 28 Years

There is also a Footstone to I.G. 1765, on which can be deciphered:
Afflictions sore long time I bore
Physicians all (possibly in vain)
When death......................
To ease me of my pain

Interestingly, although there is clearly a space left beneath Isaac's epitaph, there is no mention of his wife.

Around the corner are the finest tombs in the churchyard. They belong to the Matravers family; the owners of the name which had given the deceased Gulliver such strong suspicions. They cluster tightly at the front of the church on its northeast flank, tucked in close to the chancel wall.

The Church of St. George, Semington.

In Memory Of Isaac Gulliver Died Nov ye 29 1765 Aged 52 Years.

The Church of St. Mary The Virgin, Sixpenny Handley.

Autumn 1768

On 5th October 1768, three years after his father's death, Isaac, at the age of 23, married 26-year-old Elizabeth Beale, daughter of William Beale, in the Church of St. Mary The Virgin, Sixpenny Handley.

The Church of St Mary The Virgin, its stone tower retaining the late summer heat like a rich vein within its timeworn stonework, dominated the village of Sixpenny Handley. Its lichen freckled edifice, on this wedding day, shone bright in the low sun, framed in the autumn reds of another early Dorset October.

The Church had stood for 500 years, and country folk had seen clergymen come and go. Preachers - like the inn keepers - were known to all, not just amongst the village folk in the beetling thatched cottages, with bedroom windows so low the hollyhock's met the sills, but also across the sweep of Cranborne Chase and into the hamlets and farmsteads beyond. The church was constant and as solid in country society as the stone of its walls.

They all came eventually - even those that escaped the Sunday worship - the Church was there for them as it is today; for baptism wedding and funeral.

The Curate, on this day one Philip Rideout, entered the chancel and glanced down towards the guests in the nave. He puzzled over the unusual arrangements. As he waited the crowd stirred, there was a fluttering of heads peering and bodies leaning out into the central aisle.

He fumbled with his book. The bride would soon be arriving to be lit in a pool of bright autumn sunshine. The warm rays were busy now, painting the floor flags like molten gold as they tilted in low through the broad open door.

Why the marriage had been called for in such a way was a mystery. There had been no banns, instead of which he would conduct a marriage by license. Costly, he thought, and, if one were to be uncharitable, often a sign of, he cleared his throat, yes, a sign of some urgency.

Shadows fell across the distant shining floor, and the breath caught in the gathered ladies throats' as the bride entered with her escort. The dust motes stirred by her frock danced around her in the glow.

As the curate watched, the tall young groom who had been waiting by the chancel, stepped out and turned towards the bride, a look of pride swelled his face. He had adorned his love in the latest fashion; no lady had worn better.

The Curate did not know this young groom, and was puzzled by him. Was it his wealth, or the bride's father's that had arranged this wedding? Questions nagged in his mind. But they were questions he would not be seeking answers to. The young bridegroom's disposition had denied any likelihood of such a discussion, and to do so would have taken more courage than he possessed. Like others the Curate had fallen subdued beneath the big man's quietly spoken spell.

Halfway towards the chancel steps a hissed voice called the bride's escort to order. Titters of laughter broke the tension as he reached up with his free hand and removed his tri-corn hat.

"Shame on you," a female voice sniggered from the other side of the aisle.

Skin, painted dark with the sun, hair thinning, yet still long and black as his soul, the man fumbled with the unfamiliar headgear.

The curate's eyes fell on the man's hands, twitching at the hats rim as he stopped in line with the groom. The ruffian's right hand fingers, usually stained yellow with baccy from his clay pipe, were engrained dark with ink. All morning he had been wrestling with a quill, copying his name from a sheet left him by Elizabeth.

The curate, unaware of his efforts, looked up disapprovingly.

The man's coal black eyes were dead on his, a half smile drew back one side of his mouth, exposing some teeth, and one eye winked irreverently.

"Mornin', Reverend."

The curate, suddenly aware of their acquaintance, quickly averted his eyes upwards, as though seeking solace in the rafters of the Church. Good God, he thought, he knew the supplier of his port wine only too well, even though he had only seen the ruffian by moonlight. But he had hoped to keep his dubious relationship well away from the congregation, and more importantly from the sight of the Almighty, or at least until he had his story prepared and was pounding hopefully on the Pearly Gates.

Best get on, and get them out. Yes, move on quickly - that was it. He cleared his throat and raised his head from the man's impudent eyes, towards the waiting congregation.

After the ceremony Ridout stood outside the low stone porch and watched the procession leave. The smell of dung and horse sweat was still hanging thick in the air as the carts led by the bride and grooms carriage wound their way down the narrow lane towards the end of the village. The last stragglers finally disappeared behind the wall of a cottage, jutting out on a bend in the lane, and in a twinkling there was nothing but the dust and the smell to mark their passing.

He scratched his balding head underneath his powdered wig, he knew they would turn left at the old road to Sarum and head towards the Blacksmith's Arms. The day had warmed and with the thought of the cool ale which would shortly be flowing in the Inn making his throat feel dry, he swallowed, turned, and walked back inside the stone body of the Church.

The register lay open where he had left it, the ink now dry and dull upon the page.

He peered down at it for the second time, and creased his brow.

What was the brides name again? He squinted carefully at the mess on the page. Is that correct? The parish clerk had clearly written the name Elizabeth Beale beneath that of her new husband. But who is this that bore witness to the signing? Nathaniel Bestland yes; but Thomas Beach? This can't be right; one of the witnesses should be the bride's father.

Ridout tutted. The girl surely knew her own name. Let's see. He traced his finger across the paper to settle the question, then shook his head. A blot of ink covered her signature, with just the trace of a capital 'b' and a final 'e' discernable through the ink.

What a mess. He snapped the book shut, setting up a ringing echo that clattered about the open rafters, then tucked the document under his arm and walked off towards the open door.

The spoiled entry shares the register's page with three other marriages of the same year. There are no signatures to spoil on these however, as the brides and grooms were not capable of writing their own names, and all were solemnized by no more than a simple cross.

The spoiled entry.

Fortunate Acquaintance

Isaac Gulliver's father-in-law, William Beale 1714-1794, was the tenant of the Blacksmith's Arms at Thorney Down, on the Blandford to Salisbury Road - now the A354.

Reputedly Beale was already a smuggler, and legend has Gulliver joining him as a partner in crime. That is only supposition, but what is known more certainly is that Gulliver soon 'took over' the Blacksmith's Arms and renamed it The Kings Head.

What transaction took place between Gulliver and his father-in-law is unknown, but it appears that very shortly after his marriage to Beale's daughter Gulliver had somehow acquired the tenancy. This Public House was the first of many properties to fall into the young smuggler's ownership.

The former Blacksmith's Arms.

How Gulliver became acquainted with Elizabeth we do not know. It may have been through his dealings with her father William Beale, or he may have met Beale whilst courting Elizabeth. Either way, the association was, most likely, the key to Gulliver's success.

William Beale was a man of considerable importance within his community. Not simply because he was the Innkeeper, which in itself would command respect, but also, and most significantly, because he was a keeper of the Poor Book for the nearby parish of Chettle, a noteworthy task, providing an ancient and vital system of social security in the parish for most of the years between 1747 to 1782.

The owners of Chettle House at that time were the Chafins, and Beale's work brought him into close contact with reverend William Chafin, a fact which is born out by the pages of the Poor Book, where their signatures are written together.

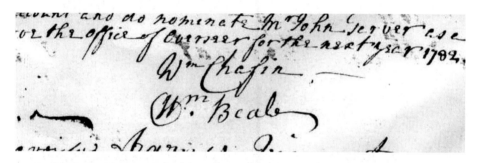

William Chafin and William Beale's signatures in the Chettle Poor Book.

The reverend William had a brother George, who incidentally plays a role in Gulliver's career later in this book, but here it is Beale's relationship with the reverend William that is most significant. If we accept that Beale was indeed the smuggler of legend, then the fact that William Chafin, apart from being a man of the cloth, was also a magistrate in the town of Blandford, must have been a gift from heaven. But not just for Beale now through a most fortuitous marriage, the association would also be ideal for our friend Mr Isaac Gulliver.

The significance of these relationships may well hide the answer to Gulliver's success. He would need a workforce, and here Beale could have proved most useful, as he of all people, through his keeping of the Poor Book, would have intimate knowledge and know every name of those in need of extra employment.

Also, it would pay Gulliver to have friends in the judiciary, and one of these seems likely to have been the reverend and magistrate, William Chafin. There is no proof of this, and we cannot say that it definitely was the case. But, we must consider it odd that in the blatant and violent acts in Hook's Wood and Blandford, recorded later in this book, nobody, it appears, was ever brought to justice.

Chettle House.

It is equally worth considering the fact that Gulliver had a great affinity with the area around Chettle, choosing to take the lease for many years of Thickthorne Farm, a stones throw from Chettle House, until quite late in life.

Here at Thickthorne Farm we can also find a link to Gulliver's network of contacts. The freehold belonged to the Sturts, land owners of Long Crichel; and Elizabeth Sturt was the mother of George Chafin and in particular the reverend William Chafin, who with Beale, oversaw the Poor Book.

We cannot know exactly when Gulliver first became acquainted with the Sturts, but it is recorded that in 1803, many years after his marriage, and whilst residing at Thickthorne Farm, he was involved in the sale of the Marianne schooner, once belonging to Charles Sturt.

   Like Gulliver, the Sturts were also in the business of carrying goods by water, although it is recorded that their ships only carried manure, lime, chalk and coals. They were the owners of Brownsea Island in Poole Harbour, and in the 1790s, seventy acres of land with a house overlooking Brownsea from the shore, known intriguingly, then and now, as Lilliput.

St. Mary's Church, Chettle.

Beale's tomb.

   William Beale died in 1794 at the age of 80. His tomb can be found in the churchyard of St. Mary's Church in Chettle. The reverend William Chafin - the last in his family line - passed away unmarried in 1818, leaving three illegitimate children.

   However, in the year of 1768 Gulliver's marriage had just begun and he was operating from the Blacksmith's Arms at Thorney Down - an ideal and prosperous location.

The former Blacksmith's Arms still stands to this day, although it is now a private family home.

   Hidden from public gaze by a dense line of trees, the place has an ageless rural charm and elegance. Indeed many of the ancient original features, which would have been apparent during Gulliver's lifetime, remain remarkably un-spoilt.

The house could well pre-date Gulliver and his father-in-law Beale by many years. Some of the timber frame construction within the walls suggests that the original building may date back to the 16th century.

Inside, the house is now a comfortable family residence, but little imagination is needed to feel the history seeping through its very fabric. The beamed front room - which was no doubt the heart of the tavern - is dominated by an enormous inglenook fireplace. This structure fills one wall, and benches within it would be sought after on a cold winter's night. The room extends to the back wall of the original inn and here situated in one corner, is a substantial bread oven.

This oven had a domed top, which stopped just below the ceiling. When carrying out repairs, many years ago, this feature gave up some fascinating links to its past. At the hidden back of the dome, among the dust of centuries, were found several white clay pipes, and, more excitingly, a silver shoe buckle. These articles had found a warm hiding place. But how they came to be there, and just how long they had been hiding in their cosy corner, can only be guessed at.

A comparatively recent extension has been added to the back of the house, this contains a pleasant kitchen working area. It replaced a previous lean-to or out-shot. Although this is now gone, a peculiar feature of it still remains in the modern kitchen. The old lean-to was built around a window in the back wall, which looks into the house. This window is tiny and is positioned at a height for a seated man to peer through.

Gulliver's Window.

It is known as 'Gulliver's Window'. From its unique vantage point, a man in the safety of this back room had a perfect view. The window is strategically positioned so as to look straight through the openings of the house to the front door on the other side of the building, and unwanted guests could be spied on at leisure. It is well named then, and fits our smuggler's character beautifully.

Two extremely low, but broad, doorways stand close together in the dining room. One leads to the front door and stairs, the other leads down brick, timber nosed stairs, to the cellar. This is a splendid vaulted room, which runs the width of the house - ideal for keeping the inn's beer barrels cool, and a perfect store for contraband.

Across the yard at the rear of the house, the stable block remarkably still stands. Aerial photographs taken many years ago show that this building was once thatched. After this came a period in which it was clad in corrugated sheeting, but now the barn is tiled. Running from its corner and enclosing one side of the courtyard sits an ancient cob wall, protected through the centuries, beneath a clay-tiled roof.

This courtyard is a quiet place today, but little imagination is needed to hear the ring of hammer on anvil, and the clatter of hooves on cobbles, as Mr Gulliver and friends entered and left, on their clandestine, illegal and highly profitable business.

By coincidence or design, the Blacksmith's Arms stood only six miles to the west of the hamlet of Tidpit. This ancient settlement, once larger than the small cluster of cottages one can see today, sits astride the old post road that ran from Poole Gate through Cranborne to Salisbury and eventually London. The road, where one can still see the milestones, was one of the major routes to the west of England and would have seen countless coaches and passengers traveling through.

*Milestone on the old road
to Salisbury from Poole Gate.*

It is an idyllic place now, but in the 1700's the hamlet had a darker side to its character, with a reputation for being a clearing-house and distribution centre for illegal contraband goods.

On the road to Cranborne from Tidpit's crossroads, stands Folliotts farmhouse. The high end-gable window, looks up towards Windmill Hill. It is glazed now and functional, but one story relates that was not always the case.

Many years ago it was in fact bricked up to stop its illegal use, for the smuggling of tea. From its raised vantage point, it was the perfect place to signal the 'all clear' to smugglers who would wait hidden in the tree-cover of the hill, before descending in safety with their contraband goods.

Across the crossroads, on the old route to Salisbury, is Angel Lane, formerly Anger's lane, which today very soon becomes no more than a track. The Angel

Inn may well have stood beside this lane. There was also a malt-house, no doubt to serve the Inn, plus a field, referred to as Hop Garden.

It is natural to associate smuggling activities to areas close to the sea, and yes, in part, this was certainly the case, but, once the goods were landed, the ships would leave the shoreline as fast as possible. Then the organized gangs would take over, covering great distances across the Dorset heath-land, some with animal drawn carts, but many on foot, literally carrying the contraband like pack horses, on backs and shoulders, to the secret inland stores.

The carriers, called 'tub-men' were paid on arrival by the weight that they carried. Quite simply, if a man could carry two kegs of brandy, he could earn over ten shillings in one night, which was perhaps a shilling more than he could earn by legal means in one week.

The work was no easy task. These men and women worked the fields by day, rising early and toiling until sundown. Many were poor and undernourished from a meagre diet, and few, when Gulliver was a young man, would have had shoes on their feet to protect them from the sharp flint and thorns of the secret tracks and the dusty Post Roads.

The route to Tidpit was no easy stroll. The hamlet lies over 17 miles north, as the crow flies, from the sandy beaches and dark chine's of Poole Bay.

Ancient Cuts in Kinson Stone

One village that was most certainly populated by smugglers was somewhat closer to the 'landings', and more convenient. Then it was known as Kingston or Kingstone - the name has somehow changed over the years into Kinson - and sits only five miles inland from the coast. By all accounts it was a well-used and notorious rendezvous.

St. Andrew's heathstone tower.

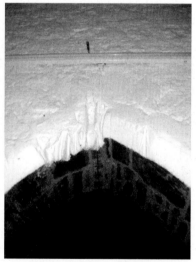

Deep cut marks in the apex arch of the tower door.

On the northern outskirts of the village, still flanked to this day by lush meadowland, stands the ancient church of St. Andrew - an unlikely but reputedly well used centre for the smugglers' moonlit activities.

The square 12th century Norman tower, built out of dark rust-red heathstone, would presumably have made a good landmark against the night sky, but that was not its only attraction. The tower and possibly other parts of

16

the church are believed to have been used during Gulliver's time as a store for contraband goods.

Evidence of the method used by the moonrakers to haul up the contraband into the church is fascinating and still visible today, and there can be little chance that Matthew Wasse B.A, the encumbent clergyman from 1738 until his death in December 1775, would have been unaware of the tower's use.

Rope cuts in the tower?   *The Oakley family tomb.*

In order to raise the goods up into their secret hiding place, ropes were thrown over the parapet of the tower, between the castellations. These ropes would then drop down inside the tower before changing direction, to rub underneath the apex arch of the inner tower door, which leads directly into the body of the church. Here, the smugglers could form a tug-of-war line in the central aisle of the nave.

One can imagine the goods, like dark ghostly shadows, swiftly ascending the outer wall, before disappearing mysteriously into the inky silhouette of the tower.

Over the years this activity caused the ropes to cut deep tramlines into the soft stone of the parapet and the door arch. However, the damage, then as now, is not visible from the nave, but, if one entered through the tower door and carried out a rudimentary search, it could not have gone without notice.

There are also stories of a tunnel running below the church which led out of a shallow incline behind the churchyard, and of a false tabletop tomb. The tomb, which has been moved, and now resides to the left of the porch, was said to have been fake and actually no more than a smugglers' store. It is in fact the tomb of the Oakley family, and its alleged use is a fanciful story with no real evidence, and possibly started because the family were acquainted with Isaac Gulliver.

However, the graveyard does bear witness to a very real event which took place on the shore between Poole and Bournemouth, one month before Gulliver's twentieth birthday.

St. Andrew's Church, Kinson.

Barbarous Murder
on the North Shore of Poole

I t was night-time, on the 24th March 1765, and an unnamed lugger had pulled away from the coast of Poole, leaving just as swiftly as she had arrived. In fact she was moving before the whalers had left her side, and was hell bent on a good wind for France. Eyes straining from the shoreline, as she headed back to the Channel, saw the tall ship now as no more than a shadowy blur against the blustery horizon.

These days the blasted Royal Navy Cutters were becoming a nuisance, and she needed to be away fast. Unlike the land bound customs men, you never knew where this new threat from the sea could strike, especially at night.

She had been right to waste no time. As she disappeared into the squally night clouds, the 'Folkestone', a Royal Naval Cutter of some speed, dropped anchor just round the point of the chine. Neither ship was aware of the others existence, they had avoided each other by mere chance.

It was a typical March night, warming with the length of the year on land but still as cold as ice on the water, and on this night the brisk wind was driving the temperature down still further.

Aboard the 'Folkestone', Lieutenant Down watched the boats being lowered. A sharp squall made him pull his collar up against the sides of his face, whilst below him, as he shivered in the draught, he heard the first whaler slap down onto the dark choppy waves. He had chosen thirteen men to accompany him ashore. Another routine search, but Christ it was chill.

They clattered down the side, swords and muskets hampering their progress. A strange job to be sure, they would scour the shoreline and the wooded chines, where the wind would be less cold, then back to the relative warmth of the vessel, and with luck, some sleep before dawn.

The tall ship creaked in the swell as they left her side, and soon the only noise was the crash of the sea striking the bow and the metronome beat of the oars as they dipped and rose in a steady rhythm of spray.

Ashore, not far down from the approaching whalers, twenty men concealed by a spit of chine, worked with low voices in the near darkness. Enough light filtered through from the scudding clouds for them to manage their task.

The waiting horses, spooked slightly by the gusting breeze and the crash of the breakers, scratched at the sand. Their hooves were eager, like the departed ship, to be moving. One of the men, holding a reign, comforted the animals with soothing soft words.

From twenty feet, at beach level, nothing was discernable with any clarity, and men, horses and bundles of contraband tea blurred into the indistinct slope of the low cliff beyond. Above them, in the lighter shade of black cast by the night sky, a few pines stood like ghostly sentinels on the top of the slope. These were the first markers on the route to a hidden dip of land known as Pug's Hole, which lay amongst the trees, a short distance inland.

The men had worked this spot before, and would soon be buckled up and away with their fortune.

On beaching their craft a little way up the sand, away from the breakers' pull, the Folkestone's crew began their search of the grey shoreline.

Midshipman Robert Wilson, and Lieutenant Down's clerk, Edward Morrice, split away from the main party, and headed towards a dark spit of a chine, just discernable two hundred yards to the south, beneath a crop of tall trees.

The soft sand coloured the toes of their wet sea boots a paler shade of grey as they trudged up the rise of the beach, towards the deep shadow. The stiff breeze, although warmer now that they were ashore, still blustered around, snatching at the grasses on the landward dunes.

Twenty paces on, Wilson stopped and grabbed at Morrice's sleeve. He held one hand up to his mouth, and inclined his head. There, on the wind. He listened intently. Yes. He was right; it came again, rustling noises, and low voices, carried from behind the chine, fading and rising, on the gusts.

"My eyes, but we're in luck tonight, Morrice." he hissed and crept forward to peer into the darkness of the little sheltered valley.

Morrice dropped low and followed.

From their position midway up the beach they found that they were in line with waiting horses. The darkness fused the beasts together into an indistinct knot. Most had been loaded with goods, their packs making them look grotesque against the scudding night clouds. But the nearest horse, sensing the visitors and jittery, wore nothing but reins.

The two men strained their eyes into the night. They could not see the man on the other side of the animals, who had been left to tend them. But on their left towards the paler shore, a few shadows, gloomier than the sea, flitted dark and ghostlike in and out of their vision.

"What now?" Edward Morrice spoke low, close to Robert Wilson's ear.

"What now? Well, look man. The horse." he gestured in the blackness. "'Tis a godsend. I shall take it and ride in amongst the curs. By god, they'll pay for robbing me of my sleep. You watch me if I don't." He turned his head towards his companion. "'Less of course you want to?"

"'Tis your plan Mr. Wilson. Good luck to you."

Wilson needed no more bidding. Sloping low across the short divide, he swung onto the back of the empty horse. He was still unaware of the man who stood quietly at the other side of the packed animals. And, as he rose above him, they were both startled.

The smuggler stepped back with an oath. One of the pack animals reared onto its hind legs in alarm, and Wilson kicked his heels into his mount's flanks and crashed past.

There was no saddle on the beast, and Wilson bounced awkwardly on its slippery back as he rode in amongst the smugglers. Once amongst them, he realized his mistake; he had seriously underestimated their numbers.

"I arrest you in the name of the King!" he cried, as strong hands grabbed the reins of his horse.

"Oh arrhh. And who might thee be then?" A broad man pushed through the surrounding crowd and stood close by the horse. Low laughter spread amongst the audience.

Wilson ignored him and recited his lines.

"And I hereby seize these goods."

"Arrhh, well then," The heavy man, known as Robert Trottman, eyed Wilson's uniform in the darkness, "perhaps you'd better take them then, my fine young sailor man." He turned to the crowd. "What's think lads?"

The crowd fell silent.

Wilson swallowed. No sound came to his ears bar the breakers on the shore and his own pounding heartbeat.

"Well," the broad man's teeth flashed in the dim light. "I takes that as a no then. So, I guess if there's any seizing to be done, tis I who'll be doing it."

From his hiding place, closer to the tree line, Edward Morrice could just make out Wilson's shadowy outline. He had appeared to stop amongst a knot of moving indistinct shapes. Morrice strained to see what was happening, then clearly heard Wilson's command blown back to him by the chilly gusts of night air.

As he watched, the dark shapes changed their form, moving in closer like a black swarm around the horse, and as they did so Wilson appeared to rise up with a cry of pain, then to fall into the heaving pool of bodies.

Cries and thuds like mallets striking leather drifted up to Morrice's ears. It was obvious to the ships clerk what was happening to the midshipman, and although he was not a fighter he could not stand by and witness his shipmate's beating.

Foolishly he ran down the slope, the deep soft sand dragging at his great leather boots, slowing his progress as though he was running in a nightmare.

Dark forms turned towards him as, panting with exertion, he reached the scene. The shapes, he could see now, were clearly men, and one of them, it was Wilson, lay still on the sand, knees pulled up to his chest, hands over his head.

Dear Christ, what had they done to him?

Wild eyed, the ships clerk Morrice, drew his pistol and waved it around. One of the smugglers broke from the scrum and lunged at him, gripping his pistol hand. Another lurched in, swinging the heavy leather handle of his coiled horsewhip up and down in a vicious arc, slamming it into the side of Morrice's head. The clerk sank towards the ground, dazed and faint with pain. The first assailant, hanging on to his wrist, fell with him.

The pistol had been primed aboard the 'Folkestone', and Morrice had cocked it.

His fingers clenched and the hammer drove home when they hit the shifting sand.

The sound of the percussion echoed around the chine.

All eyes looked towards the two bodies.

Slowly, the smuggler pulled his arm from beneath Morrice's still body, wriggled up in the soft sand, and knelt beside him. Blood oozed from the clerk's chest, spreading in a flower of darkness across his linen blouse.

The smuggler turned his head and wretched into the shadows.

Trottman pushed through the crescent of men. "My God, the man is dead."

Around him the men had stopped as one and stood like statues, staring down at the sprawled figure. At his words a general muttering of oaths rippled through the crowd.

"Tis a bad thing," he rubbed his chin, "but we cannot leave him here with a ball in his chest."

"Then best let the sea have him Bob," came from a tall shadow on his left.

"Aye you're right." The heavy man lifted his gaze from the body and turned his head towards the sound of the surf.

"We'll pitch the poor wretch into the breakers. The sea can do him no harm now, but god willing twill shield us from miscarriage."

A chorus of approval met his words.

"Then be quick lads. Come on. Look lively. Where there's two there may be more."

Woken by Trottman's words, four men urgently lifted the body and stumbled under its dead weight down the gentle slope. Once in the water they waded out through the pounding waves until they were waist deep, then in the longer swell, gently laid the Ships Clerk face up in the icy sea.

As the Smugglers turned back towards the shore their attention was taken by a vague line of figures a little way off. Shadowy forms of men, fading in and out of the oblique night, were moving fast across the firm sand, heading towards the chine.

It was Lieutenant Down and his men from the 'Folkestone' Cutter. He had heard the snap of Morrice's pistol carried down to him on the stiff breeze, and concerned that two of his crew had headed in the direction from which came the shot, had decided to investigate. The sight of bodies moving about among the waves had fuelled his fears and quickened his haste.

The smugglers had no idea what was afoot, but sensing that the running figures may be 'the revenue' strained every muscle towards the safety of the beach.

In their urgency none cared to look back. If they had then they would have born witness to the coming to life of the floating corpse.

Morrice's eyes had suddenly opened wide like traps. The ball had only grazed his chest, not deep, but enough to cause the blood to pump freely. Now as the cold water enveloped him he had woken from his feint.

His mind raced, recollecting the fight, then his head went under the waves. My God they had thrown him into deep water to drown him. He flailed his arms and legs in panic, his clothing filled with the eddying tide and dragged him down.

His head went under again.

Memories began to flash.

Then his feet touched the sand. Relief flooded through him, and he uttered a prayer of thanks.

The same water was still holding the smugglers back, dragging at their saturated clothing as they waded back to land, and by the time they reached the shoreline they could see that the 'Folkestone' men had closed the gap considerably, and were now only a few hundred paces off.

Legs tired and weak from exertion, the four smugglers finally staggered up the rise into the dark spit, one of them gasping out a warning.

Behind them, the dark shapes of Lieutenant Down and his twelve men from the ships company rounded the point in pursuit.

But the darkness of the chine was intense, causing the Lieutenant to slow cautiously to a walk, before leading his men up the rise. As he progressed, his quarry slowly unblended from the shadows and emerged from the darkness.

He stopped ten paces back, hesitant and unnerved by the size of the gang who had turned to face him. Not a word was uttered.

Behind him the ship's company had fanned out, hands on pistol butts', breath coming fast, they looked to him nervously and waited for their orders.

He had to act now. Swallowing hard Lieutenant Down filled his lungs. These lawbreakers were brazen. He licked his dry lips. But they were his prize and by God he would take them.

"Halt in the name of the King, or we shall fire upon you!" His words carried more conviction than the unfortunate Wilson's. But all they were met with were curses of defiance and a swift movement by the gang towards the waiting horses.

The sound of pistol hammers clicked in the darkness.

Clearly these desperate men would not stop without the use of force. He would stop them at all costs.

"Fire!" Lieutenant Down screamed.

Pistol shots rang out in uneven staccato, horses reared, whinnied and bucked with fear. But save for a few holes in a bale of tea, every ball missed its mark.

"Right lads," the heavy leader of the gang faced the ship's crew, "tis time to leave." Around him, the smugglers without transport had gathered in a knot.

"Take the horses," he shouted urgently over his shoulder to the horsemen behind, "and make off, fast."

At his words the beasts began to move up the slope towards the darkness of the trees.

Lieutenant Down thought fast. Damn. His powder was used and he was in danger of losing the goods.

"Right men." He yelled. "Hamstring the horses."

His men, charged as one up the slope, two slipping past the smugglers and drawing their sabres. Blades flashed in the dim light, raking down in vicious hacking arcs onto the lower back legs of the frightened horses.

Animals screamed and fell, writhing in panic and pain, sending up clouds of powdery sand. Their burdens crashed with them, flying and bumping among the startled smugglers.

A flash of light and crack of percussion rang out, dropping one of the Revenue Men with a shot through the leg, whilst the other went down, struck from behind with a heavy blow.

But the damage had been done. Nine horses lay bleeding and dying on the sand.

Just below them, in the entrance to the chine, the main body of the ships crew were struggling at close quarters under a rain of fists and heavy handled bull whips.

Trottman was in the thick of it, laying about him, one sailor's head pinned under his left arm as he downed another with a curving right hook.

"Tis fair game now lads," he bellowed, eyes glinting with anger at the treatment to the horses. "Come on then you tars, step up to the mark if you're man enough."

He punched the head of the trapped man again, dropped him like a discarded puppet, and lurched forward, roaring like a bear, into the tangle of fighting bodies. He could have taken most on his own.

Another shot filled the night. His roaring stopped. Heads turned. The heavy man staggered. The shadows pulled back from him. He fell to his knees, both hands clutching his chest, then very slowly toppled into the waiting sand.

All fighting stopped. It was as though an unspoken signal had reached every man's ears. Now, the only sound came from the surf and the dying horses.

Lieutenant Down, still on the lower slope, stood stock-still and watched a shadowy figure known to the smugglers as Isaac Gulliver, push through the crowd and kneel beside the fallen leader. A hand reached out and felt for life. Seconds slowly crept past. The shake of the head was just discernable.

"My God, sir. You have killed this man." The quietly spoken words came clearly through the night air.

"This was a good man, sir. Worth ten of most,"

the Lieutenant felt the man's eyes boring into his,

"and you have taken him from this world. Aye sir, you have taken a life, just as sure as you had pulled the trigger yourself. You have robbed a wife of a husband, and you have robbed her children of a father. May you rot in hell for your King's taxes. An innocent man lies dead here. And for what? For a leaf of tea."

A low muttering stirred in the crowd.

Lieutenant Down said nothing, just watched as the tall man rose from beside the corpse.

In the smuggler's hand a pistol had appeared. He raised it swiftly, arm straight, cocked the hammer, and pointed the wicked stubby barrel at the Lieutenant's heart. The movement was fast and purposeful. No one dared move. Eyes watched mesmerized, waiting for the percussion. Seconds dragged past, then Gulliver's low voice sounded again, above the breakers beat.

"Draw your weapons lads."

His words were followed by the cocking of pistols and swish of steel on leather as blades left their sheaths.

"Now then. This is the way it will be this night." His arm stayed straight as a ramrod. "You. Sailor boys." He shouted over his shoulder. "Back down here where I can see you."

The revenue men disentangled from the shadows and shuffled past him onto the shallow slope of beach.

"We do not want to take your lives, tis not our way, but by God if any man moves, we shall cut you down like dogs."

The silence as he paused was broken only by the sea.

Lieutenant Down's men had loosed their pistols, and he had no way of telling how many flintlocks bore down on him from the higher ground.

"We are leaving this place now." The smuggler spoke again. "We will take the horses you have left us, and poor Robert's body. And that is all. For you can have your tea. Aye sir," the Lieutenants head had moved at the words, "tis poison now, and would soil our hands to touch it."

Lieutenant Down made no reply, just stood with his men and watched as the Smugglers gently lifted their fallen comrade and backed off into the inky confusion of the wooded chine.

In seconds the smugglers had melted into the trees. All that remained on the disturbed sand were the bundles of tea, the dark shapes of the fallen horses, and the bruised, but conscious, body of Midshipman Robert Wilson.

During the affray the Ships Clerk, Edward Morrice, had fought his way back through the breakers to the shore. Once there he had hidden himself, wet and shivering in the darkness, at the foot of another chine, until eventually joining the other revenue men, loaded with contraband, on their way back to the 'Folkestone' Cutter.

Next morning, Lieutenant Down, made his report of the incident to the Poole Collector of Customs. After which, and following legal advice, he then traveled to Parkstone to inform the Parish Officer of the death of a man on his shore, and informed him of the need to contact a coroner. Also, if called upon, the Lieutenant informed the Parish Officer that he and his men would make themselves available at short notice for questioning.

However, the lieutenant had not reckoned on the cunning and speed of the smuggler's response. The Ringwood Coroner already knew of the death, and the very next day traveled down to North Haven House in Sandbanks, where at 2 o'clock that afternoon, he proceeded to convene an inquest.

Pushing his glasses back up onto the bridge of his nose he now looked up apprehensively from his papers.

"And what is your verdict." His reedy voice cut the rancid air.

The room in front of him was packed with men of a kind not usually seen on the jury side of a courtroom box. At the doors others stood guard. A small knot of evicted locals were gathered outside.

"Our verdict sir?" The softly spoken chairman replied. "Tis plain to us. This was willful murder."

A muttering of oaths rumbled around the room.

"Aye, willful murder sir," he paused "by persons unknown."

As he sat back down the noise of the crowd grew in volume. It disguised the nervous Coroners audible sigh of relief. He adjusted his glasses nervously and eyed the quiet young chairman with respect. A good verdict, yes, it would put an end to the sorry affair, no smugglers implicated and a resounding snub to that fool Lieutenant Down. To kill a man for contraband would not do, it would not do at all.

"Then so be it " he pronounced. "Murder then, by persons unknown, it shall be."

He cracked the gavel down and rose. The sooner he could get back home from this wild place now the better. Back to the gentility of Ringwood; to his cosy parlour and his keg of Port wine.

They buried Trottman in the churchyard of St. Andrews in Kinson, and that black March night on the North Shore of Poole Bay is etched into the stone of his epitaph. It reads:

To the memory of
ROBERT TROTTMAN
Late of Rond in the county
of Wilts who was barbarously
murdered on the shore near
Poole the 24th March 1765.

"A little tea one leaf I did not steal,
For guiltless blood shed I to God appeal.
Put tea in one scale human blood in tother
And think what tis to slay thy harmless Brother."

The stone is very real and can be seen in the Churchyard of St. Andrew's in Kinson, the parish boundary of which extended to the shoreline where Trottman died.

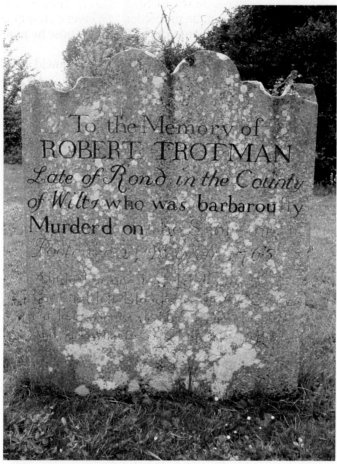

Robert Trotman's gravestone.

The story leading up to the tragedy is based on fact, as are the names of the King's men and the conclusion of the court, and whilst no other smugglers were named, it is very possible that one amongst them was our man - a young Isaac Gulliver a natural leader of men.

Path up through Canford Cliffs Chine.

Old Post card showing the stream running through Branksome Chine.

The entrance to Canford Cliffs Chine.

Isaac Gulliver's wife Elizabeth bore him two daughters: Elizabeth, born in 1770, and baptized February 4th, and Ann, baptized April 22nd 1773, both in Sixpenny Handley. Then, in the year of 1774, Gulliver's wife bore him a son. This boy, like his father and his grandfather before him, was baptized Isaac.

It was on the 24th November in this same year that we learn that the King's Revenue men were by then well aware of Gulliver's operations. And the following Official's report, written in The Poole Letter Book, gives a flavour of the growing size of Gulliver's business, and the frustration felt by the Preventive Officers in their battle against him.

It reads... *'that Isaac Gulliver, William Beale, and Roger Ridout run great quantities of Goods on our north Shores between Poole and Christchurch.'*

It goes on to report ...... *'that Cullen (another notorious Smuggler) in his Lugger Smuggles on this coast, but they all say they never could observe the sailors in the Smuggling Boats had ever any Fire Arms. Indeed we do not see they have any occasion for them, the Land Gangs being so very numerous, who have all Great Sticks or Horse Whips, with lead or iron at the Butt Ends, that it is very dangerous for so small party of Officers to attack them or their Goods, and since the Party of Dragoons that were lately Garrisoned on this coast have been ordered off, the Smugglers are become more insolent than ever.'*

Speculation and the name of Isaac Gulliver were no strangers and by the year of 1775 he had begun to build a portfolio of property and land in strategic locations. These included land at Ensbury and Cudnell, and amongst other properties in Kinson he had acquired Pitts Farm. It is not known if the Kings revenue men were aware at the time of Gulliver's growing empire, and indeed as he still operated under the guise of a humble Thorney Down innkeeper, it would have been salt in their wounds if they had.

But it was in the following year of our Lord 1776, that Gulliver made a significant purchase, which in itself speaks volumes about his brazen character.

William Chaffin, on the event of the death of his brother George, had sold him a property known as North Eggardon Farm.

This farm, which lies some six miles from the coast as the crow flies, has within its boundary one of the highest places in Dorset, known as Eggardon Hill. This giant rise in the land towers above the surrounding countryside and on its very top are the clearly defined rings of an ancient Iron Age fort. From these earthen battlements the coastline to the south and the approach towards the summit are clearly visible.

Gulliver's reason for securing the property was breathtakingly simple, the hill had been bought specifically for the smuggler's trade. Not only could

Gulliver, or his accomplices, see the contraband Lugger's arrival, but the summit was a clearly visible landmark for the gangs once they had landed.

It is possible of course that Gulliver had been using the hill for smuggling purposes for some time. He was no stranger to the Chafins, and as we know they were indeed neighbours, being the owners of Chettle, just a short distance from Gulliver's notorious Inn.

Gulliver is credited to have planted tall trees on the hills summit, but there is no visible evidence of this, and today it is carpeted by a meadow of grass and wild flowers, buffeted by the ever-present wind.

The area is stunningly beautiful and on the side of the winding lane, known as Spyway, which rises up from the village of Askerswell to Eggardon Hill, sits the ancient Spyway Inn.

This reputedly haunted Inn once housed the village forge at its western end, was licensed in 1745, and during Gulliver's time went by the name of The Three Horseshoes. The Inns, two-story, whitewashed walls appear to blend into the hill as it rises with the slope of the deep-cut narrow lane.

It is known locally as once being a Smugglers haunt, and little imagination is needed, in this atmospheric place, to see Gulliver and his men raising their tankards to another successful run.

Eggardon Hill.

At some time during Gulliver's career his men are said to have become identifiable by powdering their hair white, a practice which gave rise to them being known as White Wig's. This is thought to have been an impudent snub at authority, as hair powder was an expensive commodity and usually only worn by gentlemen, their ladies or their servants, on special occasions. Hair powder was not taxed however until William Pitt's act in 1795, which reduced its use considerably.

Some folklore has these White Wig's wearing shepherd smocks as a kind of uniform, and other stories suggest that they dressed as the servants of gentlemen. Both of these of course may be fanciful, and as they are legends neither may be true, but the free-traders in this book - like other men of fortune - will be choosing more of a dashing line in attire; it will certainly be more fitting beneath their powdered hair.

Not surprisingly, some of Gulliver's compatriots were also prepared to break the law in other ways than smuggling. One of these souls, working as a servant to the household in the Thorney Down Inn, was just such a man. His name was Levi Payne and one day, in the spring of 1777, he decided to take what was not his, not just from anybody mind, but from his Master, from Isaac Gulliver himself.

Now, it is received wisdom that to steal from a thief is not the wisest of tricks, and in this case it could not have rung more true. The news of the theft would have swiftly spread, like a cornfield on fire, through the length and breadth of the County.

Gulliver had acquaintances and contacts everywhere, many relying on his trade and organizational flare to keep food in the mouths of their families. So, on the farms, in the stables and in the roadside Inns, which were the Smugglers' hotbeds of information, the word would be out, and the hunt on, for the traitor in their midst.

Levi Payne, servant, was on the run.

He had not robbed his Master by halves, but was guilty of absconding - on March 14th - with one of Gulliver's horses, and a small fortune in cash, which he had received on Gulliver's behalf. The likelihood is that he would have traveled on the horse to collect the money for his master, and that the sum once received would have been a great temptation. For he had his hands on the then enormous sum of £21-16 shillings, which was doubtless more money than the poor servant would have ever laid eyes on in his life.

This was indeed no trifling sum. Prices have risen 126 times between 1750 and 2001, and in the middle of the 18th century, one 21st century decimal penny would have had greater purchasing power than £1. How much this servant was paid can only be guessed at, but a farm labourer could keep a family for less than 10 shillings (50 p) a week.

So he had made off with the money, which was bad enough in itself. But taking the horse as well, when men were hung for stealing sheep, would most certainly seal his fate. The authorities in the 18th century did not take a lenient line, and for these crimes they would gladly hang him twice.

But what about Gulliver, what would his reaction be on that day? A man of cunning and resourcefulness, and with a well earned reputation to keep. His brain would be racing. The last thing he could afford was loss of face. Any weakness shown on his patch and his smuggling empire would be challenged by those thinking him easily fooled. No, he could not let this theft from his own household go. That would not do at all.

Of the actual fate of Levi Payne there is no written record, and so it can be assumed that the authorities neither caught him nor brought him to trial. In fact the only way that we know of the theft at all is most curiously by Gulliver's own hand, when he chose to advertise the theft in the Salisbury and Winchester Journal.

This was curious indeed, as why on earth would Isaac want to broadcast the story? After all his reputation was surely worth more than his financial loss. The certainty is that Gulliver would have had a good reason and more likely also a complex one.

Whatever Gulliver's rationale the advertisement reads as follows:

WHEREAS on Friday the 14th of March last LEVI PAYNE, late of Tilshead, in the county of Wilts, absconded from his master Isaac Gulliver, of Thorney-Down, in the County of Dorset, and took with him 21 l. 16s. in money, which he had received on his said masters account, and a bright grey Nag, about ten years old, rises very high before, and is thin quartered behind, is galled on the near side, just behind the shoulders, about a hands breadth, and has a short Nag tail. The fleshy part of the tail has been slit with a knife, and is healed up again, the mark of which may be seen by parting the hair. Whoever will apprehend the said Levi Payne, so that he may be brought to justice, or give information of the said grey nag, so that the owner may have him again, shall receive a handsome reward and all reasonable charges, from Isaac Gulliver of Thorney-Down, near Cashmore.

The advert would have us assuming then that the miscreant had indeed escaped, and with Gulliver's cunning, that could have been its purpose. For just how far could Levi Payne have got? After all he could not have chosen a less noticeable means of escape than a 'bright grey' - a nearly white horse? Did he check the horse's shoes before leaving the stable, and did he have luck on his side? To escape the county would have needed that in spades.

If caught his punishment would have been swift and probably final, whether at Gulliver's own hand or by that of one of his allies. In which case those that needed to know of Levi's fate would be well aware. Whilst others, of the law-abiding fraternity, would assume that the humble innkeeper was still searching for justice.

The Blandford Raid of 1778

Early on a cold spring morning in March 1778 the Excise men struck back at Gulliver's empire.

Venturing eastwards from their base at Blandford towards Salisbury, they had found and seized nine casks of liquor and in excess of three quarters of a ton of tea from Thorney Down, in the very heart of Gulliver's kingdom. A brief newspaper report in the Winchester and Salisbury Journal on the 30th March reported the incident, but gave no names. However Gulliver was still resident at The Kings Arms, Thorney Down and it is inconceivable that he was not party to the ensuing events of the day.

That afternoon Gulliver's soft voice was raised and strident. "Prime your pistols lads. Them Gobblers needs some teachin'." A roar of approval echoed round the affronted mob that had gathered in the stable yard of the Kings Arms.

"Aye, hone your blades," Gulliver spoke again, his voice rising above the mob to cut the still afternoon air. "Bring clubs. And Joseph..." He stood taller and caught the leather-aproned blacksmith's eye, "bring a stout bar, for we go fully armed this day."

Beale's horses began to enter the cobbled yard, brought in from the paddocks by the stable hands. Iron shoes clattered on the cobbles, and saddles were buckled, whilst all around the air filled with the sweet smell of dung.

The beasts, sensing the excitement, grew agitated and jittery, eyes wild, snorting and whinnying as the men worked around them. In the centre of the yard Gulliver wheeled his huge frame up onto his bright grey mount. The animal bucked onto its back legs then settled.

"To horse, men."

The sun had cracked through between the gables of the old inn's roof and caught his crimson coat in its dying arc. He studied the sky, then kicked his heels into the grey's flank. "Tis time. We shall reach Blandford Forum by sundown."

The large posse, followed by a horse drawn cart, clattered out onto the great post road and headed west towards the reddening clouds. But their progress was little more than walking speed. Gulliver, mindful of the need for surprise, would pace his march to coincide with the darkness of the early spring evening.

At the sight of the first milestone Gulliver left the front and headed back down the flank of his advancing column. Most were farm labourers and he was pleased to see that, after his call earlier that day for them to join him, many had found time to don his favoured livery.

He stopped and waited, his horse pawing impatiently at the gritty surface of the road as his troops rode past. They were dressed like no other men of their profession. Fancy tunics and clean breaches with polished boots were riding by, all different colours and styles, but attired nonetheless as fine landowners' servants. However, they were in one respect very much in uniform, for each rider had powdered his hair white. These were Gulliver's 'White Wigs', and they were the revenue men's nemesis.

"Roger," Gulliver called, as a man on a black mount jogged into view.

The man, Roger Ridout, pulled out of the pack and reined in on the side of the road next to his bidder. He was as tall as Gulliver but slimmer built. Gulliver turned his head to look into Ridout's shrewd eyes.

"So, know ye where it's to then, Roger?"

"Aye tis bonded as we thought Isaac. The supervisor has it."

"So, tis in his house?"

Ridout shook his head. "Tis not that simple. He has two entrances. One leads into his hallway; t'other at one side of the house leads into a sealed warehouse and cellar."

"So tis in there then."

"Aye Isaac, behind great doors and a fancy catch, fit for a castle."

Gulliver took his eyes from Ridouts and showed his teeth in a grin.

"Well, young Roger" he was pleased with Ridout's knowledge. "Tis well we came prepared then. They Kings men will wish it were a castle, time my White Wigs have done with them."

Gulliver kicked his grey mount's flank. "Come, you ride with me at the front."

At the Tarrant Hinton crossroads the sun had sunk below the trees, and by the time they reached Pimperne with just two miles left to ride, the light had completely left the sky.

Soon their destination, the market town of Blandford Forum, lay before them, and by a quarter to the hour of seven the large body of well-armed horsemen began to clatter past the fine houses, slowly, inexorably riding towards their goal.

Some of the men spoke in low tones as they progressed. The town's buildings could not have been in greater contrast than their own lowly cottages. Around them tall houses with fine symmetrical windows, lit warmly from the inside, lined the streets. These houses and indeed the town were still virtually new. Blandford, having been rebuilt after the second of its disastrous fires, had risen from the ashes to the credit of two local architects and politicians. It stood now before the smugglers, a personification of the wealth contained within its Borough.

"Tis a rich town." One of the two men on the cart lent across to his companion, his voice just loud enough to be heard above the rattle of wheels.

"Arr and getting richer," came the rumbling reply.

"How so?" The first man flicked a rein.

"Milton Abbas. Have ye not heard, tis almost gone." The companion looked round at the questioner. "Arr tis a bad thing they be doing. My cousin lived there. They evicted him and knocked down his cottage so they did."

"No?"

"Arr they did, him and many other folk, an' they won't stop til they're all gone. Tis that swine the Earl of Dorchester, my cousin says, too untidy, he don't want them on his land, so he's a building a little village elsewhere, he says, and the folks of Milton Abbas can just go hang."

The other man tutted above the sound of the cart.

"Arr, tis true, my cousin and many like him, as has a trade, have no choice. So it's Blandford they uses now" he spat over the side onto the metalled road, "and tis getting richer by the minute."

Following Ridout's directions, Gulliver turned his horse from the descending slope of Salisbury Street and led his men round the sharp bend into the narrow rise of Whitecliff Mill Street. On the lower corner stood the Kings Head. Laughter was coming from within, but as the gang began to ride past, and the light from the Inn's greasy windows illuminated their whitened hair, all jollity stopped. Silhouettes behind the glass watched curiously, then burst into a chatter of excitement. Some had seen the revenue men bring their bounty into town earlier in the day; others had heard. It was the talk of the town, and rumours were rife. They piled out of the Inn, tankards dripping, as the procession stopped just a little way up the street.

The riders were massed outside the Supervisor's house. The doors Ridout had described stood firmly locked, and apart from a tell tale chink of light through one of the ground floor shutters the house appeared dead.

The column stood and waited, heads turned, as Gulliver adjusted his Tricorn hat, before spurring his horse along the front of the house then back again past the slither of light.

He stopped at the front door. In the relative quiet his horses shoes rang loud on the stone slabs of the pavement.

Then he reached down and gently raised the iron knocker, tapping twice.

Sniggers broke out from the gang.

Gulliver held his head to one side, listening politely towards the door. But not a sound came from inside the house.

"Knock knock, Mr Supervisor."

The sniggers turned to laughter. Echoed by some of the mob from the Inn who had come to watch.

"Well I guess you baint got the strength left to come to the door, with all that stealin' of other peoples property you been doing." He shook his head and showed his teeth, but the smile did not reach his eyes. "It's not right that, not right at all, see. We've had to come all this way just to get it back." Gulliver paused, listening again for movement, his horse snorting and constantly shifting its hooves on the slippery stone.

"Still, I heard say some good can come from a bad deed," he resumed, then turned his head from the door towards his men, "So we shall be a takin' what's ours, thank you sir," he paused again, "and whatever takes our fancy."

Cries of agreement met his words as men dismounted.

"Joseph," Gulliver called to the blacksmith, above the din. "Turn your key in that lock."

Within minutes the blacksmith's iron bar had snapped the steel clasp and the heavy doors slammed against the walls of the house as they were thrown back. Within was total darkness. Lanterns were brought from the Inn, and the Smugglers entered. The place was more of a tunnel than a bonded warehouse and the end wall of the building was far from square, giving a false impression of the size of the store. But it was big enough and gave access to a cellar.

Fancy jackets and frock coats, laid to one side, and sleeves rolled, the smugglers expertly formed a line, their goods swinging in rhythm from one pair of strong hands to the next.

Sweat beaded on foreheads and the powder from their hair ran with the droplets, streaking their faces white and ghostly. But it mattered little, if their ghoulish look put fear into the hearts of their enemies, all the better.

Just as swiftly as they had begun, the smugglers were finished, and as the last man came out he was greeted with a cheer by the mob of onlookers that had swelled in number. They had gathered up and down the street, with those opposite the Bonded Warehouse loitering by a low garden wall, behind which stood a fine red brick house. Some were already drunk, others just in high spirits at the unexpected entertainment. They had little respect for the taxman, he was a blight on them, and his humiliation was as sweet as a flagon of mead.

Gulliver had stayed on his horse all the while, stood to one side, quite still, watching the street and listening. So, where were the revenue men? No doubt the Supervisor was behind his door, and Gulliver could not blame him for staying there. But where were the rest? It was as well they stayed away. In fact he could not wish for better. Yes, he had the numbers to take them, but the revenue mens' discretion was a Godsend. No lives would be lost; just the Supervisor's pride.

Gulliver rode across to the wagon. It was groaning under the weight of goods, stacked high, and White Wigs' were throwing straps across the load.

The crowd fell quiet at his approach.

"Hold hard." He spoke softly to the smugglers, up on its deck. " We'll leave 'em two casks." He inclined his head towards the curious faces of the crowd. "Untie 'em and set them down for this mob."

He turned away from the cart and shifting in his saddle to face the mob, produced his flintlock pistol, raising it high above his head. The last of the white wigs swung up onto his mount as he turned. Good. He suppressed the flicker of a smile. They had finished their work and were ready to retrace their steps.

"Tis a fine night in Blandford my friends," Gulliver addressed the crowd, "and a rare one, for the taxman for his trouble has bought ye a drink."

At his words the two carters rolled the barrels, with kicks from their heavy boots, into the centre of the mob, and he released his shot like a thunderclap into the dark sky.

A puff of white gunpowder smoke haloed the weapon's muzzle as he held his arm aloft. Then, his horse wild eyed and bucking at the explosion, Gulliver spurred his way towards the front of the column.

Cheers sang out from the mob, accompanied by bright flashes and a tuneless cacophony of pistol shot from the White Wigs as they wheeled into line and began to clatter back down the shallow slope of White Cliff Mill Street.

In their wake, the crowd had gathered around the brandy. Smoke hung all about them. It permeated the air, filling their nostrils with its acrid sweet smell, before sinking lower, ever lower, finally reaching the cracks in the fabric of the Supervisor's fine house.

As it drifted under his front door and coiled along his hallway, it carried with it a clear message. It was a message of disdain for the authorities and of defiance of the King's taxes.

In the leather bound volume of the Blandford Forum Court Of Record, no mention is made of the events of that night. However, it does name the Constables sworn to execute their duties. There were just two; one was called Robert Snooke, whilst the other went by the title of Robert Ridout.

Another name, in a position of some importance and also employed by the Borough for many years was a Mr John Beale 'Hayward', an official in charge of fences and enclosures.

Of course, Dorset was far more sparsely populated then than it is today, and many families extended throughout the county. How close the ties between these families were we can only guess at, and there may be no link whatsoever to the incident.

But it is interesting nonetheless that these surnames, Ridout and Beale, also belonged to two of Isaac Gulliver's notorious and well documented smuggling associates.

The Bonded Warehouse doors, Blandford Forum Museum, Bere's Yard, off the market place.

The former Bonded Warehouse, Whitecliffe Mill Street, Blandford Forum.

Tricks of the Night

The smuggling fraternity, constantly at threat by the authorities, would need to have employed devious methods to avoid investigation.

One trick, legend has it, was to station a ghost. A young girl, dressed all in white, would be positioned by the churchyard gate. This would keep the superstitious villagers shut behind their doors, and no doubt be a frightening apparition in the moonlight to any snooping revenue man.

Another story tells of a further haunting image, set to chill the blood and send folk scurrying for their homes. Horses hooves would ring between the cottages and houses of the narrow streets. The sound heralded an awesome sight. At the wrong end of the day, in the semi-darkness of dusk, sweating, black-plumed horses drawing a sinister hearse would clatter by on their way to the grave.

But the coffin within contained no corpse. It would be filled with contraband - it was the smugglers ideal means of transport.

The hearse, hired from a Poole livery stable, would travel sedately through towns and villages, then journey down the lanes between them at a smart gallop. Imagine the faces of the peasants working the fields as they caught sight of this macabre apparition. No doubt they would fill the taverns that night with tales of impending doom and dark superstition.

The smugglers tracks were also said to have been concealed by local drovers. After a 'run' these peasants are said to have assisted - no doubt for payment - by driving their animals across the tracks and lanes obliterating any tell tale traces left by the smugglers on their journey inland.

Women were also involved in the contraband trade, some actively working with the gangs and others being collaborators by association. Stories tell of some of these ladies using their charms, to draw the authorities away from the action when a 'run' was on.

The ladies' targets were the officers employed by the Crown to seek out the smugglers. These men were first introduced in the late 17th century to combat the illegal export of wool from our shores.

They went by the name of Riding Officers. They were despised by the villagers and likewise by the Customs Commissioners, who, by some accounts, held them in low esteem and were unimpressed by their performance.

When these unpopular officers rode out from their billets to carry out their searches, they were known as ride-outs.

In Gulliver's time a supervisor would ride out with them and if necessary take with him a party of mounted soldiers.

Legends convey that when a 'run' was on, the smugglers' ladies would attempt to waylay the officers and keep them occupied. Whether in meadow, barn or Inn would matter little, as long as enough time had passed for the goods to get well clear.

It just could be that this was a perk of the job for some of the more lonely officers. And it certainly beat a confrontation with the 'landers', who would no doubt issue a bruising if impeded in their work.

One of the penalties of these encounters was the illegitimate child which sometimes ensued. It was a risk that went with the job, and one yarn tells, quite unkindly, that these children were consequently known as Ride-outs.

But the name was not new. It had been in circulation since the middle-ages, and was given to men on horseback who rode around the country collecting dues for monasteries or supervising Manors.

By 1779 Gulliver had acquired the White Hart Inn at Longham. An ideal location as the Inn, still standing and in popular use today, is but a short distance across the meadows from St Andrew's Church and the outskirts of Kinson.

The White Hart, Longham.

It was from this Inn that Gulliver had advertised in the Salisbury and Winchester Journal, on the 29th March 1779, the forthcoming sale of twenty 'good' hack horses. They were to be auctioned on the 12th of April.

Curiously the same number of horses, 'upwards of twenty' to be precise, were also mentioned in the same issue of the newspaper. They were reported to have been carrying, on the 19th of March, smuggled goods past Cranborne towards Hook's wood, Farnham, which is, unsurprisingly, just a few miles from Thorney Down.

No link is reported to have been made between Isaac Gulliver and the violent episode which unfolded on that day. But once again it was his patch, deep within his territory, and the outcome fits his profile like a glove.

The Battle of Hook's Wood, Farnham

Another springtime, and it was cold and damp below the dripping spinney. From somewhere above the unseen sun was reluctantly casting a pale light, illuminating the wood with a grey drear, its luminescence too weak even to decide upon a shadow among the naked twigs and branches.

But the light was enough, indeed plenty to see by, and although the steam from the horses, which had leant life to the still air, had vanished with them, the tumbled mass of smuggled goods they had left behind for collection remained clearly visible.

It stood in the centre of the clearing beside the rough track. It was unguarded, but it was not alone; seven pair of eyes had lighted upon it with satisfaction. The Excise Man and his six heavily armed Dragoons had found their goal. It was a rare thing and hearts beat faster.

Their approach had been on foot, leading their beasts through the wet undergrowth, leggings soaked and feet sodden, the leather of their riding boots drawing in the water like a sponge in a pail. They stopped on the edge of the encircling trees and looked in.

The Excise Man tucked his fob watch back inside his tunic. It had turned a quarter to the hour of four. They had been searching the woods since midday, and he was about to give it up as just another fruitless effort. But now, incredulous at his luck, he imperiously held up a hand, crouched down and scanned the tangle of undergrowth through squinting eyes.

All appeared empty of human life.

The Dragoons stood quietly behind him and watched with amusement. One, a seasoned scout by the name of Dick Smith sniggered softly, dug his mate in the arm with his elbow, and imitated the Excise Man's actions.

" P'raps we should all kneel then Will," he whispered behind a hand to his companion. "Then mayhap they wont be a'seein' us." The Dragoon grinned and adjusted his white-rimmed tricorn hat. "Might see the poxy horses though." The steaming beasts loomed behind each scarlet-coated Dragoon.

The Excise Man, ignoring the Dragoon's low voice, slowly rose. Could this be right? Was there no one here?

He scratched irritably at his crotch, then peered again. He couldn't be sure. But had there been a movement, a ghost of mist on the far side? Gone now though, as fast as it had appeared. It was his eyes, he told himself, rubbed them again as he had done so often that day, and turned back towards the Dragoons.

But he had been right. His eyes, tired though they were through lack of a good night's sleep, had not deceived him, and the ghost had risen with its heat from behind one of the broader trees, where old Hookey King had been relieving his bladder.

The sound of the spattering on the leaves had hidden the Excise Man and Dragoons' approach, but, buttoning up his flap, Hookey caught sound now of the snorting horses.

Odd, that, he mused, still fumbling, shouldn't be coming from that direction. Wrong way. Hookey peered round the trunk, and pulled back fast.

One glance was enough.

Jesus! Dragoons.

The red tunics and white trousers stood out clear and dangerous just across the top of the pile of smuggled goods that Hookey had been left to guard. Dropping low and keeping the cover of the trees between himself and the enemy he sloped off, as fast as his old legs could carry him, towards 'the barn'.

"Lucky old bugger", he muttered. Had he not needed to answer 'the call', he would scarce have escaped. He straightened when far enough away and began to trot. The barn would soon be reached; shielded by the same copse, it stood in the lea of the trees, tucked in tight to the corner on the very edge of the meadow.

Within minutes the back wall of 'the barn' loomed ghostlike through the branches, and, greatly relieved, Hookey stumbled down the final tangled slope towards its safety. Coming from the unseen front of the building drifted the sound of voices, then, penetrating above the noise of his own gasping breath, came a familiar laugh. Wheezing, he rounded the corner of the barn and near collided with its owner.

Will Sly stood foursquare at the open barn door, boots sunk deep into the mud. Behind him two other men loitered, pewter tankards in their fists.

"Whoa there, Hookey." Will Sly's smile vanished at the sight of the puffing old man. "What's on my old son?"

"Excise Man." Hookey wheezed. "Dragoons with him."

"Followin'?" Will Sly slapped the club he was carrying into his left palm and shifted his boots in the mud.

"No."

"Thank Christ, man, Get yourself in quick."

Will Sly stood aside and let Hookey stagger through into the cavernous, dark, hay-sweet smelling barn.

From the dim light within, white haired men turned towards his silhouette.

They had heard the commotion and raised voices but not the gist of it, and every man knew that Hookey King, in his agitated state, would be unlikely to be bringing good news. Tankards lowered slowly, and John Beale, filling another from a raised barrel, let the tap run on, spilling dark foaming ale onto the hard mud floor.

Hookey scurried past towards his master, Isaac Gulliver, who sat on a hay bale in the dim light against the back wall.

Gulliver's head had turned, like all others, towards the old man.

"Hold hard Hookey lad." He raised a finger, turned back to his task and pushed a neat pile of silver shillings across a board mounted on a pair of crude trestles, towards the eager fingers of a youth in rags. The boy had been the last in line to collect his pay.

"You've done well lad." Gulliver's voice was low. Then with a conjuror's touch a bright sixpenny bit appeared between his fingers and he placed it gently beside the stack. "And see you get some shoes lad" he drew his hand back, "for you're no good to me with broken feet."

The youth scooped up the coins with a "Thank ye sir", and Gulliver nodded dismissal gesturing him away.

"Now then, Hookey", Gulliver didn't look up. "Sit ye down."

Hookey took the hay bale seat opposite, vacated by the youth. All around the men had gathered closer.

"What news, old son?" Gulliver's calm voice, low and resonant, echoed softly from wall to wall and threaded through the rafters of the great barn.

Fifteen minutes of the Excise Man's timepiece later and the clearing had become filled with the noise of the Dragoons at work with their catch. Buckles jingled a tuneless mantra to the snort of the horses and the slap of leather straps.

"Oh, pile it up a might higher, my good man," the dragoon, Dick Smith, who had mimicked the Excise Man's actions earlier, now aped him again.

The party only had seven horses between them, but the yawning Excise man was determined to take as much of the dumped goods back with him as he could.

"Oh yes," Dick Smith resumed sarcastically, "and remind me to thank the Lord as I prays by my bunk tonight, for our great good fortune in finding this catch for that tosspot of an Excise Man, over there."

Dick Smith stamped his wet, sore feet, and nodded across at the Excise Man, who, he could see, was ruefully adjusting his trousers on the other side of the still considerable pile of goods.

"For now, for our troubles, we shall all have to bloody walk home."

He slapped the load that his friend Will was buckling to his horse.

"I just hopes this tea will be comfortable."

"Oi, careful, you daft bugger." Will's load, still unsecured, wobbled precariously as the snorting horse jittered and backed up. "You'll have the bloody lot off." He pulled a strap tighter, then stopped in his work, pushed back his hat and thought for a moment. "Still can't believe the buggers left no lookout."

The question puzzled the Excise Man as well and he had feverishly primed his flintlock pistol then his Fuzee, a short-barreled musket he had brought with him, strapped across his back. The vicious weapon stood at an angle now just behind him, the barrel resting against a rotting stump, its butt half hidden in the wet grass. His nerves were jangling, made worse by weariness.

He rubbed at his eyes again and tried desperately to remember the sequence of events that had left him in his present condition, but only snippets were breaking through into his confused mind.

It was that damned woman's fault. Yes, it had to be her, hadn't it? He had met her by chance the previous evening in the alehouse. A niece of the landlord? His mind blurred, and he shook his head to try to clear it. Whoever she was, he remembered her soft body falling against him, spilling his drink, her smile as she sat on his knee, then the landlord insisting on bringing him a refill. But from there on, as the beer had flowed, came nothing but confusion. He had no idea how he had bedded her, but that he had, he was sure of.

Broken visions came back to him in bursts of vivid clarity, but now more in pain than pleasure. He scratched again, and prayed to God she had not passed him the 'French Disease'. Damned woman. He twitched with the thought. Then a dreamlike vision of her leaving, silhouetted against the morning light from a grimy window, flashed across his senses. Had he slept then? He rubbed his eyes again. Christ, Jesus. Then had come the banging and the door splintering as the Dragoon burst in to drag him from the bed with news of 'the run', which he, the Excise Man - damn it - had known was scheduled for that very day.

And God. How his splitting head had pounded.

His confusion hammered back at him. He shook his head and rubbed again at his bleary eyes.

How had he come to be in the garret of the alehouse?

Why did the landlord deny having a niece?

And how had the blasted key to the garret door become mislaid?

The bemused landlord was quite at a loss.

God. What a mess.

Damn that woman.

The Excise man picked up his Fuzee from where he had leant it, and glanced across at the red coated Dragoons. Thank God - he breathed out and yawned again - that they had searched for him where he had last been seen or he would likely still be slumbering.

There had been little enough birdsong in the dripping wood when the Dragoons had started to load their catch, but now there was none. Unknown to them, the thick undergrowth surrounding the clearing, was no longer empty.

Running a short distance from the barn then splitting up, the smugglers, using the dense trees for cover, had closed in on all sides, until they were within spitting distance of their enemy. The unsuspecting Dragoons and the Excise Man had become completely surrounded.

Gulliver, his broad frame and red coat hidden by a thicket of holly, waited patiently until he judged his White Wigs to be close enough. Then, at his shout, they attacked as one.

In seconds they had joined in battle. The Dragoons, seasoned soldiers to a man, swiftly drawing their broad swords against the smugglers' steel tipped cudgels. Shouts and war cries filled the clearing. Horses reared and screamed with fright, knocking men to the ground with their flailing hooves. Tea bales flew from the mounts' backs, striking men indiscriminately on their way to earth. A brandy keg crashed down, splitting wide, soaking the air with it's heady tang.

"Christ, they're like man-servants gone mad!" The Dragoon mimic, Dick Smith stood back to back with his friend Will. The powdered hair and gentlemen's servant's tunics of the attacking smugglers was unnerving.

"Shut up, and fight." Will faced two White Wigs. He parried a swinging stick, then was brought down with a blow from another.

Dick Smith also had two assailants. They stopped swinging their sticks, stood back, and smiled.

"Here, Will lad," Dick grinned "I think my two might be friendly."

He stepped back, and fell over the prostrate body of his friend. The last thing he saw before passing out was another Will; Will Sly, hair white with powder, grinning broadly as he brought down his club.

Across the clearing, the remaining four Dragoons, now hopelessly outnumbered, formed a protective knot around the nervous, twitching Excise Man.

Blood chilling curses sang out above the sound of wood on steel. One Dragoon staggered onto his knees with a cry of agony, his sword scything the air as it left his hand. A cudgel had broken his fingers. He fell headlong, gasping and reeling under a hail of blows.

The remaining three fought on, parrying some attackers, taking bone-crunching blows from others. Blood flowed from split faces and broken hands as they fell back.

It was only a matter of time. The Dragoons were losing fast against the overwhelming odds. With luck they would take a beating and escape with their lives. But then, the Excise man, unused to 'the fight', decided to take a hand.

A cannon's roar filled the air. He had triggered off his murderous Fuzee. Flame shot between the flailing broadswords as the red hot ball found its mark in a smugglers arm, sending him spinning out of the fray.

The Dragoons' hearts chilled at his actions. My God, what had the fool done.

Acrid gunpowder smoke filled the air.

He then released a shot from his pistol. The flintlock fizzed, flashed and cracked an angry bark around the clearing.

Another smuggler staggered back as the heavy shot slammed into his chest. The ball ripped through him. His back exploded through his fine frock coat, in a fountain spray of blood, bone and sinew.

Furious at the Excise man's stupidity, the Dragoons cursed him more than their relentless attackers, for they were now convinced that he had sealed their fate.

Choking on the gunpowder smoke, they fought on, finally going down under a hail of sticks and cudgels.

Now, in the wet grass, they lay huddled together, knees drawn up, bloody heads, shielded by their arms, and waited. The Excise Man lay with them, felled by a dozen sticks, and spat on where he lay. The two other Dragoons had been dragged across and dumped close by.

The Dragoons had not set out to make war against their own countrymen. And they had certainly not set out to murder. No. Not for a bale of silk or a keg of wine. After all, smuggled goods for the gentry were common currency.

But now a life had been taken, and maybe another lay in the balance, and that, they knew, demanded revenge. The conscious lay fearfully now, waiting for retribution.

A quiet had descended in the clearing, then a soft low voice from somewhere behind the smugglers drifted across to the fallen men.

"Leave them be now lads."

It was Isaac Gulliver. His words carried clear through the damp air.

"Enough blood has been spilled on this day. And more killing won't bring no-one back from the dead." The jittery horses snorted and stamped a tattoo behind his words.

"Aye, and think on, for if any man needs a killin' then it can only be the Excise Man. For 'twas he that pulled the trigger."

Shouts of "hang him" rang out.

Gulliver's voice rose.

"No. No man wants to see him swing more than I." He held up a fist "Aye, I would rather break his neck with my own hands. But I cannot."

The crowd muttered.

"For if he dies," Gulliver continued, "we shall have to kill them all, or they will bear witness, and the King's men will hunt us down like dogs." He paused. "You think on it lads."

His resonant voice lowered again.

"No. The man lives, God rot him, and the Devil can wait to burn his soul."

Oaths of agreement rumbled around the clearing.

The Dragoons' swords were snapped between stout branches of the trees, and their flintlocks broken and flung into the undergrowth. Horses were brought and repacked, and the smugglers left the clearing taking their dead and wounded and the Dragoons black horses with them.

Within the hour, birdsong returned to the woods, and the seven King's men, who had all regained consciousness, were alone, bloody and broken, but alive and free.

The party would no doubt have returned on foot to Cranborne. The Dragoons, who were most likely men of the 6th Inniskilins, either to their billets in town or to sick quarters at their main base in Salisbury under the command of Lieutenant Colonel The Lord Robert Ker. It would all depend on the severity of their injuries.

As for the Excise Man, he would have made his report, and ridden himself or sent a rider for assistance to the nearby market town of Wimborne Minster.

His only victory came the next day, when a party of Dragoons from Wimborne swooped on an Inn and took two men, reported to be smugglers, from their beds. Unsurprisingly, the Inn was situated on the main Blandford Road, the location of Gulliver's notorious Blacksmith's Arms. The two men were committed to Dorchester Gaol.

However the Excise Man's victory was short lived. Four months later, in the month of July, two men were reported to have been tried at the Dorchester assizes. They were accused of being smugglers and '*of taking goods from some officers of excise.*' Predictably, no evidence could be found to substantiate the outrageous accusation and both men were duly acquitted.

Some time before this acquittal, and in fact less than ten days after the battle, the horses taken from the party by the smugglers had all been retrieved; a telling move by the smugglers. For they would not consider themselves to be thieves, the theft of goods was not their game, and these men were not cutthroat pirates. No, the horses were taken in order to give themselves a clear run. Once far enough away from the Excise Man and his Dragoons, who were on foot and injured, the horses would have been released, to find their own way home. After all, these beasts were of little use to the smugglers. They were instantly recognizable as the mounts of the 6th Dragoons, jet-black and all of a similar height. Indeed it was the horses, which gave the 6th their nickname, 'The Black Dragoons'.

The above is based on a historical event, although the detail and the affliction of the Excise Man have been added. However, whilst at the time Gulliver was not implicated, it bears his hallmark; no man killed; all goods rescued; no smuggler convicted. A good result in fact from a master tactician.

A private in the 6th Dragoons as he would have looked in 1779. These Dragoons all rode black horses until 1796 when the authorities decided that it was no longer possible to get a black horse for all the cavalry.

A Most Notorious Smuggler

In the Year Of Our Lord 1780, Isaac Gulliver's name appeared again, in an official report in Poole after revenue men had raided Mr John Singer's Kinson granary. The report, which appears to be concerned with John Singer's character, is revealing. It makes clear that by now the tax collectors were well aware of the extent of Gulliver's activities. Also, by its tone, the letter discloses a growing frustration.

It reads as follows:

'From the best enquiry we are able to make into the character and circumstances of Singer, we are informed that he has been long concerned in the Smuggling Trade, and it is said he is a servant to Isaac Gulliver a most notorious Smuggler, ...'

Two more official written reports were sent in 1782. They were initialed, and as the last initial is a 'W' it is possible that they were written by a Mr Weston, who was then either the Collector or the Comptroller at Poole. The first report, copied below, was made on the 13th March to the Customs Commissioners.

'And we have humbly to observe to Your Honours that we are of opinion that large quantities of wines are run on this coast, particularly by one Isaac Gulliver a most notorious Smuggler, who lives at Kingston near the sea shore and is professedly a wine merchant and the better to conceal the frauds on the Revenue, which he carries out enters and pays duty for some part of what he imports, and by mixing that with what is run we are informed he bids defiance to the officers to seize any wines from him, and they have not in any one instance been able to detect him; which is humbly submitted by
13ᵗʰ March 1782   Hon' Sirs, Yours... J.L.W.'

This last missive shows even more frustration than the report of 1780. But, oh what joy the revenue men must have felt at the next report, sent to the Customs Commissioners On 11ᵗʰ May 1782, listing details of smuggling offenders and seized goods.

'Honoured Sirs,
We beg leave to inform your honours that if renewed Writs of Capias were sent us against Richard White Michael Joyner, John Fry, Isaac Pardy and Isaac Gulliver against whom your honours were pleased to commence prosecution for the offences mentioned on the back hereof, we are of opinion that we could get them arrested; which is humbly submitted by'
11ᵗʰ May 1782   Hon' Sirs, Yours... J.L.W.'

Richard White for harbouring and concealing ----- *169 galls Brandy*
8 galls Rum
168 galls Geneva
2092 lib of Tea
56 lib of Coffee

Michael Joyner -- *32 lib Tea*
12 galls Brandy
5.5 galls Geneva

John Fry ---115 *galls Brandy*
42 galls Rum
282 galls Geneva
620 lib Tea

Isaac Pardy--- *2850 lib Tea*
120 galls Brandy

Isaac Gulliver for unshipping 4 Pipes of wine without payment of duty.

(A single pipe of wine is a cask, usually equivalent to 105 gallons or 477 litres. Which would mean he was accused of illegally unshipping around 420 gallons (1680 litres) of wine.)

It can be assumed then, from this report, that Isaac had been caught red-handed, somewhere between the smuggling lugger's delivery to the beach, and one of his hidden stores. However there is no evidence of this.

The phrase used in the letter, '*renewed Writ of Capias*,' suggests that the revenue men had been somehow unsuccessful with previous papers.

Also, from the wording of the letter, it appears that it was the ringleaders that the revenue men were interested in trying to bring to justice, and not the small army that would have been needed to carry the goods ashore.

But if the Revenue men thought they had finally cornered their man they were due to be sorely disappointed, as Gulliver's luck held true to form.

There are two accounts of how Gulliver avoided prosecution. They are both quite different, but each involved King George III. Both now follow. The first tale is considered to be the most likely, and seems so typical of Isaac Gulliver's good fortune.

Gulliver's activities of course were being played out to a background of strife and overseas conflicts. Britain had been at war with France and Spain since 1778, a war destined to last until 1783, and on the other side of the Atlantic, the American War of Independence had been raging since 1775 and again that struggle was not due to end until 1783.

While these wars continued the gentry in Britain were happily benefiting from the smuggling trade, which was by that time endemic. How else would the well to do get their necessities from the continent?

As a nation at war with our neighbours we could not be seen to be openly trading with them. But the King and his parliament, who knew the game and would undoubtedly have also benefited from the odd glass of contraband, had to find a way to stem the trade. After all it was illegal, and as such needed to be brought under control. Also it was from taxed goods that the King's money was raised, money needed to finance the wars.

Parliaments' plan was simple. The Officials had been repeatedly unsuccessful in bringing the smugglers under control. So, rather than spending more money on the problem by using more troops, the King's parliament decided to offer the smugglers a truce. Indeed to offer them, for a price, a free pardon.

A proclamation to this effect was released and interestingly found its way onto the pages of the 'Gentleman's Magazine', a journal read by the well connected. Was that significant? Perhaps. The proclamation may have been aimed directly at the magazine's target audience.

The proclamation is copied below.

Gentleman's Magazine   vol L111 (52) 1782, page 258.

Friday 3rd May 1782. A proclamation was this day issued for granting a free pardon to all smugglers and others under prosecution or liable to prosecution, in prison, or beyond sea, for any penalties incurred by the illegal practices of clandestinely running prohibited or un-customed goods, who shall on or before the first day of July next voluntarily enter themselves as sailors on board any ships belonging to the Royal Navy or who shall procure one fit and able seaman and one fit and able landman as substitutes to serve for him, her or them, provided the penalty to which such persons are liable do not exceed the sum of £500: Those above and under £2,000 to find two fit and able seamen and two fit and able landmen: And those above £2,000 to find three fit and able seamen and three fit and able landmen. Upon which conditions all specified offences are to be forgiven. Likewise his Majesty's pardon to all deserters who shall surrender before the 17th June.

It is most likely that this proclamation, arriving most fortuitously on cue, is what saved Isaac Gulliver from prosecution. Imagine the chagrin of the Customs officials. Just when they thought they had the most notorious smuggler in their sights, the King had unwittingly stepped in to bale him out.

Gulliver was by this time considered to be extremely wealthy, and he would therefore find little difficulty in meeting the terms of the pardon. It could still have been tight going though as he and all others who wished to take advantage of the offer had been given just 44 days in which to fulfill the agreement.

The second tale, also relating that Isaac Gulliver had been granted a pardon, is less likely to be true. However, it makes an exciting story, paints a romantic picture of Isaac Gulliver 'the patriot' and is the stuff of legends.

The story tells of Gulliver, whilst in France, discovering a plot to assassinate the King. Presumably Gulliver was procuring stock for his trade at the time. Concerned for his King's safety he sailed home swiftly with the news, no doubt on one of his fleet of fast smuggling luggers. Once ashore he took the information to a friend at Court, who immediately told the King. Concerned for his personal safety, the King ordered spies to be sent across the water to see if the story were true. On their return with the news that it indeed was, the King showed Gulliver his gratitude.

"Then," the King pronounced, "let Gulliver smuggle as much as he likes."

Legends then attribute this magnanimity as the reason why Gulliver appeared to smuggle with impunity, opening a wine shop in Poole and being described as '*exceedingly rich*'.

Amusingly, this piece of folklore also suggests that Gulliver was very well known indeed, for it seems that even the King knew of Gulliver's clandestine activities.

It is of course possible that many people would not have been aware of Parliament's proclamation, especially those that could not read. Bearing that in mind it is easy to see how the verbal knowledge that the great man had received a pardon from the King himself would need some justification. And what better way, in the smugglers Inns and around the cottage fires, to explain Gulliver's freedom, than with this romantic and patriotic story.

In the same year Gulliver once again used the Salisbury and Winchester Journal for his purposes.

The paper, no doubt read by the Customs men, carried an advertisement, and proclamation. To them it carried the possibility of some respite, and no doubt brought a smile to their lips, and a sigh of relief, at least to those foolish enough to swallow its contents verbatim.

The advertisement reads as follows...

To be LETT and be entered on at Michaelmas next, all the DWELLING-HOUSE, with the Shop, Malthouse, Wine Cellars, Garden, and other premises, now in the occupation of Mr Isaac Gulliver, at Kinson in the county of Dorset.

For particulars enquire at the house.

Mr. Gulliver is about to remove to Tingmouth, in Devonshire, where he proposes to carry on the Wine and Brandy Trade, and hopes for the continuance of the favours of all his friends and customers, who will please to address their orders to him at Kinson, as usual, till Michaelmas next.

So that was nice, wasn't it? Not only was he moving out of the area but also announcing that he intended to *'carry on in the Wine and Brandy trade'* in Devon.

His impudence had grown with his wealth.

He knew very well that he was a hunted man and that the Revenue men were well aware of what he meant by carrying on his trade. He was rubbing it in.

However, after his announcement he may well have left his shop premises in Kinson. But not for a residence in Tingmouth (Teignmouth). In fact he had a house just over a mile to the north of Kinson, in the parish of Hampreston.

The house was Hillamsland Farm, an ancient dwelling, which stands today on the edge of Dudsbury Golf Club. So Isaac had not gone far then, and unsurprisingly in 1783 he was still trading as a wine-merchant in Kinson. Maybe *'the favours of all his friends'* had persuaded him to stay.

Hillamsland Farm, Dudsbury.

Hillamsland, like many ancient houses, has a reputation for being haunted, and even today some people who have stayed at the property have reported feeling a mysterious presence. Below the house is a sizeable cellar, which contains three former openings. The brick headers to these can just be seen. The two higher arches face east and south, whilst the lower arch faces west. What lies behind them is a mystery.

However they fit nicely with the stories still being passed down verbally through the generations, of secret passages, one running from the house, towards the White Hart Inn a quarter of a mile to the west, and another, setting out towards St Andrew's Church, just under one mile away across the meadows to the south.

Outlines of the bricked up openings in the cellar of Hillamsland Farm.

Hostilities resumed in Gulliver's territory on Thursday February 19th 1784, when Customs officers, acting on information that 'run goods' had been concealed in a barn and stable in Kinson, descended in force.

These men were not dragoons but sailors in the service of the Port of Poole, about six miles from Kinson. They were led by William Sander, Commander of the Laurel Cutter. He was accompanied by Samuel Calborne his Mate, and Richard Wilkinson, Mate of the Diligence Lugger. With them they had mustered another thirty-seven men.

One would reasonably imagine that this small army of 40 armed revenue men would have had carte-blanch to search as they pleased. But have a care, this was Kinson. Word would have flown along the route of their approach and the Kinson folk were ready for them.

As the revenue men began their search, the Smugglers, who were over 100 in number, suddenly attacked. Some were on foot and others arrived on horseback and they had come armed for the fight, carrying pistols, cutlasses, pitchforks, bludgeons and other offensive weapons. After a desperate struggle the smugglers were victorious, but typically drew short once again of taking any lives.

The Revenue men had not only been denied their search but had been badly beaten for their trouble. After losing the fight and returning to Poole empty handed they were put under the care of a surgeon and no less than 27 were confined to 'sick quarters'.

In the report that followed, the fact that none of the revenue men had been mortally wounded was considered a bonus.

During the fight, some of the smugglers had been recognized and they were named in Customs Officer Weston's official report of the incident. Isaac Gulliver's name did not appear, but interestingly, and to prove the point that the smuggling trade was not wholly dominated by men, the list contained the name of Hannah Potter, who was the wife of the local innkeeper. This suggests she had little trouble when it came to calling 'time'.

The premises run by Hannah and her husband John, was originally a 17th century coaching inn called the Dolphin, and although much altered, it still stands in the centre of Kinson today. However, the sign outside has changed and today this ancient smugglers' watering hole goes by the name of 'Gulliver's Tavern'.

Gulliver's Tavern - formerly The Dolphin - Kinson.

A Person of Great Speculating Genius

In 1788, four years after the violent affair in Kinson, information on the character of our 'wine merchant' was requested by the Board Of Customs in London. The report sent back to them from The Port Of Poole, is copied below.

Hon Sirs

In obedience to Your Order Signified by Mr Gale's Letter of the 3rd instant (No 174) for us to Report the General Character of Isaac Gulliver and the sort of Merchandize in which he is concerned; we humbly beg leave to inform Your Honours,

That but a few Years ago the said Gulliver was Considered as One of the greatest and most Notorious Smugglers in the West of England, particularly in the Spirits and Tea trade but in the year 1782, he took the benefit of His Majesty's Proclamation for Pardoning such Offences and as we are informed dropped that Branch of Smuggling, and afterwards Confined himself chiefly to the Wine trade which he carried on to a Considerable Extent having Vaults at Various places along the Coast to the West of this Port, some of which it is said, were situated in remote Places, and we are well informed that he constantly sold wines considerably under the fair Dealers Price, from which Circumstances there is no doubt but that he illicitly Imported that Article but which Trade we are also Informed he dropped some time since.

He is a person of great Speculating Genius and besides the Smuggling he has carried on a Variety of other Businesses, but we find he is not known at Present to be Concerned in any Sort of Merchandize, and lives retired at a Farm in this Neighbourhood, having acquired as is Reported a very Considerable Property. Which is humbly Submitted.

J.L.R.H.W

10th December 1788.

The letter, once again written by Comptroller Weston, reveals a certain grudging admiration, mixed with more than a hint of chagrin. In one breath it states that our man has gone straight, then tells us that there is no doubt that, since his pardon, Gulliver got rich from continuing to sell his hidden stash of cut price smuggled goods.

Could it be that the striking phrase '*a person of great speculating genius*' is Weston's way of telling us that Gulliver was just plain too quick for the authorities. It does seem very likely.

In the same year, Gulliver, still only 43 and, according to Mr Weston, now retired, was selling another property. Once again this was in Kinson. The advertisement is copied below.

TO be LETT, a neat and convenient DWELLING HOUSE, with suitable offices, a good stall stable for four horses, necessary out-houses, etc, also a large garden walled in, and stocked with choice fruit trees, a small orchard and fields adjoining the same.

The above is pleasantly situated in Kingston, near Wimborne, Dorset, and fit for the reception of a small genteel family. A pump and good water in the kitchen.

For further particulars apply to Mr Gulliver, at Kingston aforesaid. Immediate possession may be had by applying to Mr Tait, at Wimborne, the present tenant.

This advertisement states that the present tenant is a Mr Tait. He is credited to have constructed Pelhams House in 1793, which was five years after the advertisement, on land belonging to Kinson Farm. So, it is possible that Weston was referring to Kinson Farm in his official letter.

It has been implied that Mr Weston, Comptroller at Poole, and writer of the reports to the Board of Customs in London, was dismissed from his post in the early 1790's. If the implications are true he was in the pocket of the Smugglers and had been passing them information.

Possible of course, but also possible that he was a thorn in the side of his masters 'the gentry'. These were wealthy men, and many it is said enthusiastically benefited from the likes of Isaac Gulliver. They would be well positioned to have Weston discredited and removed if he became too meddlesome.

In the year 1789, Gulliver added another property to his portfolio. This new house and farm was in West Moors, which lies about four miles to the north of Kinson. To this day the property is known as 'Gulliver's Farm'. The crop gabled red brick house stands a little way back from the road with its old stable block to the front and to one side. The house has an interesting oval window on the first floor positioned centrally above the front door.

This farm would have been quite remote in Gulliver's day and like his other large acreages an ideal location for hiding contraband within its grounds. Also, predictably, the property stood on the route up country to Cranborne and onwards to the notorious Tidpit crossroads and Thorney Down.

An interesting tale tells of wide grass verges flanking the sides of the road at Gulliver's Farm. These once had deep cuts within them at irregular intervals. They are thought to have been constructed in order that the Smugglers, with horses trained to turn swiftly down the hidden tracks, could escape at speed if being chased by the law. Then, from the safety of these bolt holes, cunning eyes would watch the puzzled excise men gallop ever hopefully past. It is a nice story and the mysterious cuts in the wide grass verges, whatever their purpose, were still visible in the 1920s, but unfortunately are now gone.

Gulliver's Farm, West Moors.

Much of Gulliver's contraband would no doubt have come from certain warehouses operating in the main ports along the French Coast and in the Channel Islands. Warehouses, willing to sell to a country with whom they were at war; a business transaction that would cause little loss of sleep. After all, a sale to the smuggler profited the French.

The wholesaler and producer would be paid. The smuggler, who had a wealthy and thirsty customer base, would call again, and, best of all, the English King would not be receiving any taxes to fuel his war. French hardliners would no doubt disagree, but all in all, from the wholesaler's point of view, it was a most satisfactory business.

The ships being used to ply the Channel with the illicit trade were usually fairly small craft. These craft, called Luggers - originally used for fishing - became more developed as the century wore on, and made ideal transport. They were compact and extremely seaworthy, capable of carrying a heavy cargo, and if crewed well, could avoid the more cumbersome Revenue Cutter.

At his height it is thought that Gulliver owned 15 such vessels. Each one was capable of carrying a small fortune safely across the Channel to the landing places along the north shore of Poole.

Run with the Wind

"There be lights ahead Gem." Gulliver's voice rose above the rush of wind and icy spatter of salt stinging spray.

The taller man at the wheel grinned. His wet black face, blurred into the night. The moon had slid once more behind the fast high clouds.

The glare from the orb sparkling from the crests of the waves had hidden the coast from Gulliver. Ahead had seemed just endless dark horizon. But now in the new blackness a glimmering row of lights on the French coast twinkled faintly like dancing fireflies.

The African had been aware of the nearness of the land. A fine sailor; Gem Brown, without conscious effort, could sense the coast through the rhythm of the sea and the scent of the air.

He altered course to starboard, an experts touch bringing her round into the breeze. The moon appeared again, in time to see the massive spread of dark canvas shiver and fill as the vessel raced eagerly onto her new course.

The grin on Gem's face parted into a deep shouted laugh. The contagion swept along the deck to the crew. Hanging on for life to the low protection of her bulwarks they shouted and whooped back. A rollercoaster bow wave curled and hissed down her sleek sides, then boiled and spread as a swallow's tail from her lute stern.

She was a bird of the sea.

She was flying.

Behind his high collar, Gulliver allowed himself a smile. He had invested well.

Four months before, he had ridden to Ham, on the north shore of Poole's vast harbour. He had gone with a purpose. Timber workshops, ship's hulks and masts littered the stony ground. Fires burned. Steam, from boilers, rose in plumes, and the smell of pitch permeated the thin cold air.

Across from him a large vessel stood on props with up to a dozen men at work upon her. He led his horse across and past. He knew full well the cutter's purpose. Only the 'Revenue' would need such as she.

A blacksmith's hammer, ringing loud as the tolling of a bell, unsettled Gulliver's horse. He spoke gently, soothing the animal's nose, and walked on. Past another open shed, full of rough-cut tree trunks. Round a jumble of roofs on props and a dozen fishing boats under construction. Down a dip in the land, now only a few feet higher than the glimpse of lapping water on his left, and he had reached his goal. He was on the very edge of the activity. A barn's width of long roof propped on rough cut tree trunks filled the centre ground, and a red scrub covered sandstone cliff rose close and tight on two sides. Gulliver looked into the scene.

Tucked into the cliff was another much smaller building, a hut with its door hanging open. Its owner, Samuel Starling, sat in front with his clay pipe between his teeth. Samuel Starling, Master Shipwright, the man Gulliver had come to see. Gulliver led his horse down the sandy path onto the hard, left the animal with a gentle word at the foot of the rise of cliff, then closed to within four paces of the sitting man.

Sam Starling was sucking casually on his pipe with a feigned air of satisfaction, as though visitors were all the same to him. He didn't look up. Just blew the smoke in the direction that both men were looking.

Gulliver opened proceedings. "How goes it Sir?"

Sam sucked on his pipe. He had been expecting the visit - Gulliver called at regular intervals. "Can't grumble," he said.

Gulliver dragged his eyes from the jumble under the propped roof and inwardly raising an eyebrow, looked down at the speaker. Sam was still a young man, maybe late thirties Gulliver guessed, but he had lost most of his front teeth and what little hair he retained he grew long above his ears to drag over his shiny pate.

Gulliver knew the game. "And our business sir?"

"Tis Well," Samuel paused, "I be satisfied sir."

Gulliver could feel the man's pleasure.

"Be you now, Samuel?"

Samuel put down his pipe and stood, still looking towards the jumble under the broad propped roof.

"Best you lead on then, young sir."

Samuel made his way towards the shade under the roof. Pushed aside a few planks and a canvas screen and led Gulliver into the great hall within.

The jumble of canvas and timber on the visible sides of the building were naught but a disguise. Within was clean and tidy, stacked trestles, clamps, anvil, benches, pots, brushes and tools all neatly hung and stored by a master craftsman. Centre-stage was his work.

Samuel looked back and the twitch of a smile vanished fast from Gulliver's broad face.

Before the two men stood 'their business', a boat - a boat on props and still under construction. Samuel walked forward and stopped just before her bow, the crown of which stood several feet above his head. He ran a critical hand over the planed timber. "What's think then?" he said.

Gulliver's breath caught in the pitch and timber scented atmosphere. Truth is he had never seen anything like this vessel. Dared to dream that she could be built, yes. But now in reality, she was finer than he had ever imagined a seagoing vessel could have looked.

He said nothing in reply, just walked down her flank.

The dream had long been in his head before he first met Samuel.

"I want speed, sir. Can you give me that?" He had said quietly. It had not of course been a chance encounter. Samuel had been recommended to him as a man of great skill.

"If you want sir I can build you a boat that will fly like the very wind itself."

"And how would that be, sir?" Gulliver's voice was measured and low. He watched Samuel Starling closely.

Starling did not reply immediately but thought awhile. He knew full well who the big quiet man was that spoke with him. "I am a poor man, sir," he said looking up, "and would not wish to give my secrets for naught."

Gulliver nodded. "Nor would I take them sir."

He then placed a gold sovereign on the table between them and slid it across, keeping his hand over the coin. "But if you works for Isaac Gulliver you will find me a generous man. And," he paused, looking directly into Starling's eyes, "there will be a bag of these for your troubles." Gulliver's gaze held his man. "So shall we talk on?"

Samuel looked at the back of Gulliver's hand, imagining the gold beneath.

"Aye, sir. I would be glad to."

Gulliver left the coin. Pulled back his hand. Held it up to his mouth and spat. "Good." his eyes glinted. "Then spit on it lad. You spit on it."

Two seasons after his meeting as he walked down her flank, he could see the fruit of his investment.

Samuel had not let him down. He had used ingenuity, imagination and the latest understanding of boat and hull design, to create what the revenue men would pounce on and destroy if they had any inkling of its existence.

Gulliver reached out a hand and ran it along the smooth timber. Clinker built for lightness, the planking was pleasing to the eye. There was width to her, yes, and he could see that she could carry a cargo. But she was so different; Samuel had abandoned the rules.

This boat was not designed with the traditional 'cod's head' and 'mackerel tail', where the greatest breadth of hull was forward of amidships, no indeed, she was a new breed.

There was no broad, buoyant bow, fit only to batter through the sea. Instead she had a long slender bow - to Gulliver's eye, like the blade of an axe. From this cutting edge, graceful timbers like the curl of a wave, swept elegantly, effortlessly, down her sides enveloping her widest point before converging back gently to her flying lute stern. Beneath, her razor sharp keel sat straight and true.

Her lines were sleek, beautiful, exciting.

62

A ladder leant against her bulwarks, Gulliver climbed carefully up its worn rungs and stood on the timber deck. Looking towards the bow he could see that she was nearly ready. On Gulliver's last visit Samuel had been finishing the deck beams and mast partners.

Samuel came half way up the ladder and leaned elbows on the light blue painted bulwark.

"She's nearly there then, young Samuel." Gulliver was finding it hard to keep the pleasure from his voice.

Samuel smiled a toothless grin.

"Said as much."

The fact was, he never said much at all. Gulliver appreciated that.

The great bowsprit - nearly a third the length of the boat itself - was resting on her deck. Gulliver eyed the apparatus. Once mounted on her bow, this long pole would increase the sail capacity considerably.

He looked at Samuel. "Masts are here then?"

"Aye, and near ready. Look yonder." He pulled himself up on deck and pointed to the other side of the Lugger.

Gulliver followed his gaze. He had paid no attention to the working area on the other side of the boat. There, just outside the supporting props of the hull, two great masts rested on a dozen paint-spattered trestles. Faint sunlight breaking through the jumble of camouflage on that side of the shed dappled the timbers and the wood shavings carpeting the floor beneath.

Gulliver nodded. "They be straight and true then, Samuel?"

"Can't get better." Samuel Starling was still smiling. "Cut 'em myself last January, before the sap rose." He gazed down at the masts, narrowing his eyes as he inspected their perfect symmetry.

"Aye." He turned back towards Gulliver. "And there be seventy rings on the mizzen sir." He paused for effect, nodding. "Aye, seventy. I counted 'em twice."

Shortly, the two men returned to the step outside Samuel's shed. Gulliver did not need to see any more. He was well pleased. Now that the paint was on her hull she was ready for launching, and once afloat the masts could be hauled into place.

All was going to plan. The launch would take place at night, and many hours and many hands would be needed to get down to the water. These hands would belong to his 'white wigs'. It would not do for the wrong eyes to see her. A shape such as she possessed could only mean one thing, that she was built for speed, and therefore in the eyes of the revenue men, an illegal boat.

They would be right of course, for what fisherman or cargo carrier would need anything like the power that this boat possessed. No expense had been spared. Her vast sails designed to extend far out over the water 'for and aft', and to fill the sky above, were set to dwarf her racing hull. Her purpose was to achieve performance and ability, and by so doing to leave all others, especially revenue cutters, behind in her roaring wake.

Gulliver tossed Samuel a pouch of tobacco, produced another for himself and both men filled the bowls of their pipes. They leant back against the shed wall and smoked awhile. The thin winter sun brought a faint warmth to their faces and the tobacco smoke rose straight in the still air.

Eventually Gulliver broke the silence. Leaning his bulk forward he gently inclined his clay pipe in the direction of the sandy path, which had led him down to the 'Hard'.

"I sees the new Revenue cutter is taking shape." He was referring to the large vessel he had passed earlier. "Anything I should know"?

Samuel and a few other employees of Gulliver also worked at times on the King's ship.

"Well, seeing as how you ask, I have heard that the ballasts all wrong, for a start." Samuel tapped his pipe.

A little extra iron had been introduced one cloudy wet night.

"Oh yes", he added blowing out a satisfied plume of smoke, "nearly forgot. And the planking is too heavy. Well, they says they wants her to last. So that's good."

He shook his head. "Arr, she'll do that right enough... Trouble is," he turned towards Gulliver, "she'll sail like a barge, sir."

"No. Tis a shame." Gulliver shook his head with Samuel. Then slowly exhaled his own plume of smoke. "I just can't think where it all goes wrong."

"Still," he bravely dismissed the puzzling thought, "tis the festival of Christmas, and Twelth Night will soon be upon us, and I can't have your fine self worrying for the plight of the poor revenue man. No, can't have that, not in this season of good will. That would not do at all."

Gulliver drew a small heavy bag from his capacious pocket and placed it, from beneath his hand, covertly on the step between them.

"So make merry on me in these dying days of the old year young Samuel Starling. For in the new year we shall see our business complete."

Christmas had passed some three months since, and the merrymaking of that season was far from Gulliver's thoughts as he clung now to the wheel stand of his new vessel. The weather in the channel blew bitter, such that the cold knuckles of his hands showed white in the gloom.

She dipped into a new trough between the waves - a chill salty spray lashed his face - then rose majestically above the crest of the next roller. With the passing of the months, the hands of the craftsman had fulfilled their promise and Sam Starling's dream had taken to the sea.

The vision he had shared with Gulliver had become a reality, and they had given her a name, one which suited her well.

She was now 'The Dolphin'.

Gulliver released one hand, wiped the salt water from his eyes and looked aloft. Her sails cracked and filled as she heeled on a port reach to starboard. For the past few days a gusty sou-wester had been beating in from the America's. They were taking full advantage of it's mighty force. Gem Brown, the man by Gulliver's side, a blurred shadow in the night, had swung the wheel, hauling her great bowsprit round into the fury.

She was returning from her first exhilarating escapade across the English Channel. Her hold was packed with contraband, but even with a full belly she responded eagerly. Her stealthy speed seeming little diminished. She was flying.

The 'run' had been routine, marred only by the sighting of a revenue cutter rounding the indistinct headland in the dusk as they left the French coastline. The Dolphin was a much smaller craft, and Gulliver could not be sure if they had even been sighted. The cutter was 'beating in' nearly directly into the wind and the Dolphin was heeling hard with the wind's force full behind. She had dipped and risen between the valleys of the grey waves. In minutes the larger ship had disappeared into the murk. They had lost all contact.

The cloud cover blasting in across the Atlantic stayed with them. It concealed their passage and with a miser's grasp clung to its saturating downpour, thinking it best to pitch its misery on the coastline to the east.

In record time the tree lined shore of Bourne Heath emerged before the Dolphin. Gulliver drew a hand across his eyes. Although he was in the leeward, the salt spray had done its damage. He blinked at the stinging pain as he made out the landmarks in the inky blur before him. He had made countless 'runs' but the excitement of the landing remained a constant.

There - he saw the first pinprick of light in the darkness - then another - a candle's light flickering through the tube of a smugglers lantern.

Gem had led them in the dim night and the rushing English Channel's waves, directly to the very spot; to Bitman's Chine. Gulliver, still holding onto the wheel stand, turned his head towards Gem Brown.

Gem was looking directly at him, he was nodding slowly, teeth bared in a mocking grin. Gulliver pulled up his collar concealing his face from the crew 'forard' and barked out a laugh.

"Why, Gem lad" he shook his head, "you was six feet out. 'Tis a puzzle to me, that I keeps you on."

The shore remained some fifty yards off, they needed the depth and the space to flee if surprised by 'The Revenue'. Anchors dropped. Sails half hauled and turned from the wind, the experienced crew set to work. Half a dozen stout whalers that had left the shore un-seen, pulled in alongside. Ropes thrown over The Dolphin's bulwarks and secured, and the work had begun. No shouting of orders bit the air, no need, just the scurrying of feet, the slap of the sea on the hull, as with silence, stealth and speed the goods were swiftly transferred.

Gulliver left the Dolphin with a small crew in the first whaler, and headed for the sandy run of beach. Gem Brown crammed into the same craft, sat atop a pile of tea bales, whilst the silent crew rowed steadily into the shore-bound breakers. The eight oarsmen pulled harder at a low command as the lifting breakers began their curl some thirty feet out. The little craft hit the shallow rise of land at speed - the leading oarsmen leapt out and lifted and heaved - and with the help of the tide, they were beached; a little wooden boat, with a white hump amidships, like a strange seagoing dromedary, ridden by a black African.

The other small ships landed similarly. 'Hands', 'carriers' and 'tubmen' scurried down from the dark chine and mustered whilst the contraband was checked off and allocated. The men would be split into gangs, each gang would have its instructions, its dropping off points and its hiding places; they were organized, and run by the 'White Wigs.'

Gulliver, choosing to remain silent, stood back by the water's edge and surveyed his army. The wind blustered, slapping the collar of his greatcoat against his cheek. The surf sent fingers of foam up the beach, licking at the heels of his boots. He was 'the lander', yes, the smuggler general, of that there was no doubt, and no man questioned it. But tonight, Roger Ridout had organized the land crew for him.

Gulliver looked on with satisfaction.

The noise of the surf gave way to a faint whinny, and the sweet smell of horses made him sniff the air. Over to his left, from the blackness of the west shore, the scent and sound of the beasts had drifted down to him on the wind.

Gulliver narrowed his eyes into the darkness. Yes, he could see him now, it was The Keeper of The Poor Book, Beale. He had emerged from the shadows, a little distance off, with another figure who, from his size, Gulliver knew must be Joseph, his blacksmith. They were leading five horses. Four were pack animals. Gulliver watched Joseph stop with them by a main knot of smugglers, whilst Beale came on with another friskier animal, then stopped central beach and waited. As instructed, he had brought Gulliver's horse. Gulliver walked across, took the beast's reigns and hauled his broad frame into the saddle. He leaned forward, whispered soft words, and the white horse bucked and wheeled a half circle in the sand. It settled, pawing at the soft ground and shook its head, snorting.

Gulliver slapped the strong proud neck.

"She's in fine fettle then, William." He looked down at Beale who had backed off from the performance.

"A beauty, Isaac. And no mistake." The wind blew a greasy lock across his dark face. He brushed it away and saying no more, turned and walked back towards the knot of men. Beale cherished the beast. He would spend hours in her stall, washing, grooming and talking gently as he worked.

Gulliver followed him over. Ridout was in the centre of the knot. He left the men at Gulliver's approach, and stood beside the horse a little away from the crowd.

They nodded a greeting, then both turned their heads towards a movement in the darkness. A small pale shape had emerged from the ink black entrance to the chine and was approaching at speed. Gulliver's horse shuffled and snorted. It was a boy dressed in a shepherd's smock, running hard, sand flying, snaking in the wind like fleeing wraiths as it kicked up from his bare feet. Gulliver and Ridout were between the hastening figure and the smugglers working on the beached cargo, shielding the apparition from view.

The boy stopped, slipping to his knees in the sand, gasping for breath.

The horse snorted again, backing a pace.

"Master Gulliver, sir." The boy fought for breath.

Gulliver's broad form, greatcoat and pale horse were unmistakable. His eyes darted. Few, if any, had seen the boy's approach, and - judging it may be better to keep it that way - he leaned down towards the child, removing his tricorn hat to save it dropping into the sand. "For my ears only, lad. " He held a finger to his lips. "Now, speak you slowly."

The boy sucked in a lungful of salt air. "Father, sent me sir. Said where I should find you. Fast as I can he said." He choked another breath. "We seen em!" He nodded, eyes wide.

"Who lad?"

"Gobblers, sir. More than one hand's fingers they was. Poking about near Pug's Hole, sir."

Gulliver's eyes flashed. Pug's Hole was two miles to the northeast, and a dropping off point. He stayed leaning down towards the child, whose breath was coming more easily.

"Was they mounted lad?"

"No, but they had horses nearby sir. Black' uns"

Gulliver held a hand, palm out to hush the child, and straightened in the saddle.

"Blast. Ye hear that, Roger?"

Ridout had been listening intently. "Aye, like a bell. Black Dragoons."

Gulliver settled his tricorn against the wind. "Anyone gone that way yet?"

"No."

"Good." Gulliver rubbed his chin. "Aye, tis good. Now boy," he flicked a shiny coin towards the child, "how are your legs?" The boy missed his catch and scrambled around in the sand, coming up open-mouthed holding the gold disk.

"That coin be solid gold, lad." Gulliver fixed the little shepherd with his bright shrewd eyes.

The boy was caught like a moth in a flame.

"You hold it tight and your legs will fly like a mill sale in a gale. Now take it back to your father. Run with it. Run like the devil himself were on your tail.

And tell him this. Tell him that Isaac Gulliver is in his debt for his vigilance, and he is to call on me and I will pay him the same again." Gulliver clicked his fingers and pointed, raising his voice. "Now. Go. Go like the wind."

The boy broke from his trance, turned and scampered back up the beach. Sand flicked from his departing heels, and in seconds he was lost among the silhouette of trees on the inky ridge.

Gulliver straightened and turned towards Ridout. "Roger. Fetch me a keg of brandy and strap it to my saddle. High, so that all can see."

Ridout raised an eyebrow. "Why so?"

"Why So? Why so that the Revenue gets a good look. I shall not have them being disappointed tonight. They wants a smuggler to chase." He rubbed his horses pale neck. "Well, they will have one."

"Then I shall find a mount and come with you," Ridout said.

"No. 'tis good of you Roger. But you are needed here. You will have to divert the Pug's Hole goods elsewhere, and see the run through. Besides you'd be getting in my way. We only have the packhorses and the black dragoons would haul you down in no time, and you're good to no-one dead. No, I goes alone."

Ridout shifted his feet in the soft white sand.

"Now," Gulliver continued. " Fetch me the keg - and a pistol."

"They'll shoot you down if they see it." Ridout referred to the weapon. He was terse.

Gulliver's resonant voice came low, barely audible above the westerly wind and the crashing breakers.

"They can try."

Minutes later, loaded with one keg of contraband and a pistol, its butt protruding ominously from a saddle holster, Gulliver spurred his horse into the blackness of the chine.

Few paid attention to his departure. After all, he had no need to watch on, and Ridout had been given instructions to tell no-one about the reason for the shepherd boy's visit. Gulliver reasoned that the less the landing crew knew the better, and that they would work swifter without the knowledge that armed revenue men may, just may, try to break up the run.

Once through the steeply rising chine the trees gave way to the undulating heath. It lay bare before Gulliver, a frozen sea of stunted vegetation with the occasional twisted stump where a tree had tried and failed to survive. Gorse, its early yellow flowers turned grey by the night, showed dark among the ling, whilst all was held in the grip of the rustling wind-rocked bracken. The track Gulliver traveled down was soft under his horse's hooves. The thump, thump of their beat broke the noise of the wind as he rode. He knew every gully and turn. And he knew that with each moment's passing he was getting ever close to danger.

Soon, a darker gloom than the night sky began to unfold before him. It rose higher as he rode; he was nearing the tangled wooded outskirts of the fertile dent in the land, the wooded gully of Pug's Hole.

He reined in and stopped. Listened. Nothing. Then walked forward. The track began to enter the outer sparse trees. A night bird as pale as his horse drifted through the bower ahead. He stopped again.

"Pssst." A voice called softly, eerily, from the dark tangle a short distance ahead and to the right. Gulliver's hand sunk into his side pocket and wrapped around his hidden pocket pistol. He sat low, still as a statue. Was it the revenue calling to each other? Had he miscalculated? Why would they be in the thin undergrowth? And there was no sound of horses, no rattle of military harness. Nothing.

"Pssst," it came again, "Master Gulliver, sir." The voice was nervous. "Tis I, Thomas Barker. I sent my son to you, sir."

Gulliver's eyes darted around the shadowy leafless thicket. Had he been betrayed? He tipped the squat barrel of his pistol, still covered by the heavy cloth of his pocket, towards the voice. "Then show yourself, Tom Barker."

Immediately a man, dressed as a shepherd, rose from behind a low dark clump. He wasn't alone, the boy messenger stood up with him. Keeping low they slunk across the ground to stand beside the rough track.

The boy was grinning, shifting from leg to leg. The man removed his wide hat and stood turning it round in his hands.

"Thought you was more Gobblers, sir." He looked round furtively. "Or worse still, you might have been Pug a coming through the woods after us."

Gulliver released the grip on his pistol and withdrew his hand.

"Pug's long gone mister shepherd, and his ghost won't be a hurting nobody, leastways not this night. Now tell me man. Where be the King's Men?"

"Not far, sir." he pointed into the black woodland. His eyes shifted from the dark enclosure then back towards the ground beneath Gulliver's horse. His voice came breathless.

"Pug's Hole, sir." He crossed himself, and looked back towards the blackness. "Aye, they did open the door and went in... Seen 'em with my own eyes."

Gulliver's eyes narrowed towards the trees. People stayed clear of the woods for fear of the ghost; the ghost of Pug - Pug the smuggler.

He had been dead for many years and his hut lay a ruin in the centre of the dip in the woods. Gulliver perpetuated the story; fear kept folk away. This meant the hut had become a major dropping off and distribution point for Gulliver's White Wigs.

Had the Revenue found out? Or were they there by chance?

Gulliver looked down at the shepherd. He was a brave man for going so close. "Could you hear anything, Tom?"

"Aye sir, I could hear them clear through the trees. There was a smart one. Tall man, in a black coat, doing most of the talking. Seems someone had spied smugglers leaving these woods one night. And he had been told there was a run on but didn't know where, so he thought he would catch some tub men on their way through, or find a cache. They looked for an age but found nothing, sir."

A night bird called nearby. The three conspirators looked in the direction of the call.

"Go on." Gulliver's voice broke the silence.

"Well, there is no more sir. Only that they will still be there. Just, the tall man has a timepiece. He told the men that they would stop for one quarter of an hour, before taking the south track to the beach." He raised his head and looked up as though calculating the horizon. "My son came back," The boy nodded eagerly, "told me what you had said, and we have left not long since. So I would say they will be about ready to leave."

"Be they now?" Gulliver's voice sounded softly in the night. "I thank ye, Tom Barker." He produced the second gold coin he had promised the boy earlier and held it between two fingers down to the shepherd. "Isaac Gulliver is a man of his word and my debt is paid." He fixed the shepherd with steely eyes and dropped the coin into the eager outstretched hand. "But you must do one last thing for me. The shepherd, eyes wide at the shining treasure, nodded. "You must find your sheep sir, and find them fast, drive them over my tracks. There must be no trace that I came this way." He stared down at the man. "Is that clear, sir?"

"T'will be a pleasure, master." The man nearly curtseyed at the request.

Gulliver straightened in his saddle. "Then I bids you both a good night."

Leaving the shepherds beside the track he rode carefully into the dark tree cover directly ahead. In seconds the inky blackness swallowed him.

The narrow track he traversed, little more than an animal run, wound snakelike around the un-coppiced trees. By daylight he knew each turn, but the night played tricks. He began to drop more steeply into the ravine passing a rotting stem on his right shoulder, and he had his bearings. As he dropped, the ground became boggier. Last year's brambles tore at his sleeves, tugged the skirts of his greatcoat, and the pungent leaf mould beneath his horses hooves thickened. He knew that he would emerge from this tributary onto the main broader track some fifty paces from Pug's hut, and with luck he would be in time.

At a familiar turn in the track he stopped and listened, knowing that in the light of day he would have glimpsed the ruined dwelling that lay below him and on his left flank. The wind did not penetrate the sunken wood. He could smell the mould of rotting thatch and the stench of decomposing timbers, drifting up through the screen of tall spindly trees.

With the stink of putrid decay came the sounds of the revenue party. He calmed his horse and listened. They clearly thought they had the wood to themselves. Muttering and grumbling of the men, snorting of horses, rattle of harness and stamping of hooves concealed any noise made by Gulliver's approach. He spurred his horse on, quickly descending the last few feet, taking him past the obscured ruin, then stopped again as the narrow path met the main track.

There was more light here. The way was wider, and the track broadened further as it wound past Pug's ruined hut. There, the trees lying further apart failed to meet overhead, and whilst the setting below could not be considered brightly lit, there was light enough for Gulliver's purpose.

Gulliver tugged his tricorn tightly down, peered out from his hidden position and surveyed the scene. One glimpse was enough. He pulled back fast.

The party of seven were mustering, making ready to mount up. They were Black Dragoons and dangerous. White breeches showed clear against fine black horses. Two were already mounted, the others were milling around. He had to move fast. He pulled the vicious pistol from its saddle holster, checked its charge, carefully replaced it, walked his horse out of the cover and turned head on towards the revenue men.

He was fifty paces from them - not a man noticed.

Gulliver caressed his horse's neck, leaned forward, his cheek against her ear, and whispered. She quivered at his voice, backed a pace, then at his command she charged - fearless as a white thunderbolt - directly towards the midst of the enemy.

In seconds, horse and rider, leaping high, crashed through the knot. Black horses bucked, shouts and screams rang out, riders spilled, crunching to earth and un-mounted figures threw themselves to the ground.

Gulliver was shouting, adding to the confusion. "Clear the way, you dogs!", as he sailed over,

Landing on the track on the other side, he pulled up fast. Divots flew from the white horse's shoes as he turned her. Men were scrambling up, cursing, hats askew, some missing. The revenue man - black leggings kneeling on the filthy track - looked up, his face as white as the soldiers breeches - saw the horse, the keg, the pistol and the man above.

"My God," he breathed, "it's him." Then louder. "It's Gulliver." He waved his arms as if trying to propel his Dragoons across the ground. "It's Gulliver!" The last few letters of the name came out in a shriek. "Get him. Get that man!"

The white horse reared and wheeled, Gulliver raised the pistol, loosed his thunderclap shot into the sky and spurred the horse north towards the open heath.

In less than a minute, man and horse burst out of the dark tree cover, up and out of the cloying, tangled gully, back into the grey night. A rutted track through the gorse lay before them. The outskirts of Kinson and Gulliver's grand house stood just four miles distant. He gave the mare her head. She stretched her neck. Every muscle vibrated. Gulliver clung for his life as the Pegasus horse ate the ground beneath her flying hooves.

Outside the hollow the wind still blew. Gulliver's eyes, wet with his speed, narrowed to slits. A fox darted across the track ahead and vanished into the bracken. The horse thundered on. Gulliver's mind raced with it. They would know his house and follow, of that he was sure. Only speed could win him this game. Ten minutes would suffice. Ten minutes to safety. He willed the mare on.

The track wound down and round as the heath gave way to a lane. Pastureland and hedgerows replaced the bracken. He galloped between great oak sentinels, up the last rise, and the house, behind it's high thatched defensive wall, loomed dark ahead. The gate was unlatched. Slowing at last, he left it to swing to and made straight for the ancient stable block. Steam rose in clouds around the glistening pale mare.

"Peter!" Gulliver bellowed.

He had no need. The stable-hand had heard the hooves on the gravel.

A door banged, and the boy swung down from a trap in the stable ceiling.

"Master?" He looked at the steaming horse. His eyes traveled up to the pistol butt, standing proud of its holster.

"Be lively lad." The big man slid down from the steed. "We will have company. The Revenue."

The lad's eyes flicked back towards the pistol.

Gulliver, aware of the boys fear, began to unship the brandy keg.

"Aye, you heard me right. On my tail, and they shall be here in no time. So, remove the saddle and harness and hide them."

With the keg under one arm, he slid the pistol from the saddle holster. "Then takes the horse to the far side of the paddock. Leave it and get yourself back here fast. And remember," he caught the boy's elbow, "if the revenue asks, ye have not seen me leave this house tonight."

Leaving the boy to his work, Gulliver crunched across the gravel to the tall side-gable of the house.

The unlocked kitchen door gave silently to his touch.

Quickly, he stepped in and turned the great key. There was no light in the room save a faint ember in the vast hearth. The smell of roast venison hung in the warm air.

He swiftly crossed the room and entered the inner corridor. At the far end soft candlelight spilled from the broad sitting-room door. Good Mrs Gulliver was not abed. In ten paces he was within the room's warm embrace. Glowing logs filled the great fireplace, one fallen forward sent a whiff of smoke curling around the mantle. A fine clock sat centre place, candles flanking its polished case.

Mrs Gulliver sat by the fire, mop capped and high collared, her winged chair protection from any draft that may find its way through the room's elegant shuttered windows. She rested her embroidery in her lap and looked up.

Her husband was not expected for two more chimes of the mantle clock and the pistol dangling in its holster raised her brow.

"You are early, Mr Gulliver." Her steady eyes sought an explanation. Her voice was measured and calm.

"Aye, Mrs Gulliver," he placed the heavy keg on the oak timbered floor and grasped the edge of the rug, "and with good reason."

He began to roll back the heavy covering, revealing a trap door let into the floor. It was set close to Mrs Gulliver's chair. She removed herself, stooped and rolled the rug with her husband. "Must you hide yourself?" She placed her hand on his, and looked back towards the pistol where Gulliver had placed it beside the trap door.

"Aye, I must." Gulliver followed her glance, "But no, there has been no blood shed, my dear, fear not on that account."

"Then what can have happened?"

Gulliver wrapped his fingers around the brass ring and raised the hatch.

"There will be time," the thunder of horses broke the night air, "to explain later."

Mrs Gulliver turned her head towards the noise.

Her husband snatched up the holster pistol, and dangling the weapon down into the dark hidden room, lowered himself to his waist.

"That will not be friends, I fear." Gulliver looked up at his wife's face. "Twill be the Revenue."

With his words came a hammering on the massive front door.

"Then I shall speak with them." Mrs Gulliver grasped the hatch. "Away quickly, husband."

Gulliver dropped down. The hatch lowered over him, leaving him in darkness.

Mrs Gulliver breathed out, rolled back the rug, kicking it smooth with her foot, left the room, and hurried through to the main hall. All the while, the hammering continued. It was louder here. It hid the sound of the maid's feet descending the stair. The noise was such to arouse Mrs Willoughby the cook from her room at the rear of the house. Both the maid and Mrs Gulliver turned to see her appear from the darkened corridor on their left, cross faced and puffing, capacious shawl thrown over her night clothes.

The candles they carried threw dancing shadows on the paneled walls.

"What the devil?" The cook bristled.

But Mrs Gulliver stopped her with a glance. "Mrs Willoughby." The cook held her breath like a kettle about to boil. "As you can hear we have visitors. Unfortunately they must be allowed in, but I will only allow two over my threshold," Mrs Gulliver instructed. "Two," she repeated, "that is all, and bring them to me in my sitting room." Then she turned to the younger housemaid. "And Mary, child, quickly, run girl and fetch the groom."

The girl shielding her candle, swished into the dark inner passage. Mrs Gulliver retreated, and the cook, holding her candle before her, approached the thundering front door. It was secured by heavy bolts top and bottom. She slid them back with a crash. The hammering ceased. She turned the great iron key, threw back the door and held out her candle. The cold night air wafted her ringlets, which had escaped from beneath her nightcap. She filled the portal, fuming in her porcine majesty. She exploded.

"You strike this door once more," she shouted. "Go on, just once more," her eyes traversed the startled Revenue party, "and I shall take my hand to you."

The officer was flanked on the step by two dragoons, one had his fist up, ready to strike the woodwork again.

"You dare," she snarled.

He lowered his fist slowly.

"Right," she glowered. The revenue party stood rooted, agog. "Now, I aint never bin wakened so rude in all my life, so I haven't, so you'd best have a mighty good reason. Come on, explain yourselves."

The dragoons shuffled their feet, while the Revenue officer cleared his throat and gathered his courage.

"I demand, madam," he straightened his shoulders self consciously, "in the name of the King, to see the owner of this house."

"Oh, you does, does you." The cook stood four square, resolute. She looked the man up and down. "Well if you be a representative of His Majesty, then I pities him." Stifled sniggering came from a dragoon at the rear of the calling party. "For I doubt he would have such poor manners as thee." She paused. "Still, I shall let you in, but only because my mistress has asked me. If it were up to me I would send you, and your demands, packing, the lot of you." She scowled as a schoolmistress around an unruly class. They believed her.

She allowed two men in, as instructed, their boots suitably scraped before entry, closed the door firmly, and showed them in to the warm inner sitting room.

Mrs Gulliver was seated once more in her high backed chair. She had listened to the lambasting with interest.

"Thank you Mrs Willoughby, you may retire," she said.

The frock coated revenue officer stood just within the door; a dragoon, helmet under his arm, accompanied him. Mrs Gulliver looked closely at the officer. His tic had developed since they had last met.

It was Mr Weston, the Poole Comptroller.

"Good evening Mr Weston." Mrs Gulliver did not smile. "And what brings you to my house at this ungodly hour?" Her voice chilled the room.

"I think you are well aware of why I am here, lady."

"No, sir. I was not aware that word had spread concerning my husband."

Mr. Weston twitched. What did Mrs. Gulliver allude to?

Mr. Gulliver, beneath them, ear pressed to the floorboards, heard his wife's words with curiosity.

"It is your husband of course, madam." Weston chose to ignore his confusion. "Your husband that I am here for. He will not escape judgement this time, I can assure you of that." His eyes darted around the dark shadows of the room. "Oh yes. I have seen him with my own eyes." He pointed a finger, indicating somewhere in the distance, above and beyond Mr Gulliver. "Yes my own eyes madam, just one half hour ago. And I have witnesses to prove that he is cheating the King of his taxes."

"Then you saw a ghost sir." Mrs Gulliver's words cut the air. "For Mr Gulliver has not left this house for days."

Weston straightened his shoulders. Twitched. Opened his mouth to speak.

Mrs Gulliver carried on. "Yes sir, Mr Gulliver is at home now and not far from here, I can assure you of that." Weston turned his head, and looked out through the open doorway, into the dark hall. The dragoon, eyes anxiously searching the shadowy corners, gripped the hilt of his broadsword.

The boards above Gulliver's head creaked.

"And of course," Mrs Gulliver continued, "I also have witnesses to prove my statement sir, as you will well know. But, Mr Gulliver will not see you tonight of that I can also assure you, for he is otherwise engaged. Indeed it is to be hoped that your devil of a noise did not disturb him."

Weston opened his mouth to speak, but Mrs Gulliver rose, piercing him with her gaze, and placed her hands on her hips.

"Also sir," her words became darts, "you have no warrant to search my house for Mr Gulliver if that is in your mind." She turned her gaze on the dragoon. "And I have a witness to the fact that I have denied you permission." She looked back into Weston's eyes. "And sir, if you attempt to do so, an authority higher than yours shall hear of your affrontery."

Weston had been stung - he narrowed his eyes. "You will regret your threats, madam. For this will go to court. And the judge will decide whose witnesses are the more reliable. Yes," Weston's tic convulsed his face, "rest assured, your husband is as good as hung. I shall be back tomorrow with a warrant for his arrest."

"Do your worst, Mr Weston."

Mrs Gulliver clapped her hands, and raised her voice.

"Mr Smith," she called. The meeting was over.

The groom and the stable hand had been waiting, unseen in the unlit corridor. At her command they slipped into the room, sleeves rolled tight. Heavy sticks, tipped with steel, swung from their hands.

"See these gentlemen to the door." Mrs Gulliver's words were little more than an icy whisper.

Mrs Gulliver waited until she heard the stout bolts drawn on the front door before lifting the hem of her skirt. The fine material of her petticoat had become snagged. Gulliver had heard the bolts as well and shouted up from below. However he had to wait for release until his wife had extricated her skirts from around the keg, over which she stood. The incriminating keg that had been left in haste for all to see, and which Mrs Gulliver had kept hidden beneath her skirts throughout her clash with Mr Weston.

The following day did its best not to break. The grey squall of the night merely became a degree lighter - that was all. That was the sum total of its broken promise. Forlorn, bedraggled with a damp and chill wind, it was unfulfilled; the kind of day that would slip past grudgingly until darkness descended once more.

But it was a day which would not be without incident. Mr Weston would see to that. Mr Weston was as good as his word.

The mantle clock had not struck the midday before he had returned - he and another. He stood now outside the great front door with one of the dragoons from the previous night. Mr Weston had cleaned the dried mud as best he could from his black coat and polished his boots for the occasion. He clutched a small leather case containing a warrant.

In the light he had found the bell pull and used it - listened, to hear the resonating toll from within the main hall - then stood back from the stone step. The westerly wind tugged at his tricorn while he waited, he put his spare hand to it and looked up. The house was indeed grand. Castellations rose above the parapets and even fortified the broad porch before him. He stood before a house that could be defended.

The sound of industry and horses drifted over from the stables on the cold wind. Weston tried to ignore the interruption and listened carefully again, head on one side, towards the door. Yes, above the distant clamour he could hear the faint sound of footsteps from within, echoing from the grand entrance hall's stone-flagged floor.

A key turned audibly and the door slowly opened.

A maid stood within the threshold. She was clothed darkly. Eyes, red with tears, looked up into Weston's. She said nothing.

Weston took command. "I have come to see Mr Gulliver." He adjusted his shoulders at mention of the name.

The maid burst into tears.

"Who is it, Mary?"

Weston, confused by the girl's behaviour, recognized Mrs Gulliver's voice. It came from a distance, from somewhere in the house. She sounded tetchy.

The maid stood crying into her kerchief at the door.

"It's Weston," Weston shouted over the maid's blubbing. "I demand entry in the name of the King." He enjoyed that bit. "And I have a warrant, Madam." She would not get the better of him. Not this time.

A bustling of frocks announced Mrs Gulliver's approach. She appeared at the door behind the maid.

"For goodness sake stand aside, Mary." Mrs Gulliver's voice was terse. She ushered Weston inside.

"I have been expecting you sir. I would like to say with pleasure, although I cannot."

Weston nodded. "Your husband, Madam?" He raised his eyebrows. He would prefer to be civil.

"My husband, Mr Weston." she sighed in resignation. "Yes, he is waiting for you sir. Would you care to follow me?"

The hall was dark, save for a single candle. Curtains remained drawn and the shutters were closed as though it were night. The central fire in a paneled wall of the staircase had not been made up. There was no heat. Weston shuddered with the cold.

Mrs Gulliver led him to the bottom of the stair, to a curtained alcove.

"Here is my husband." Mrs Gulliver's voice sounded weary, beaten, not at all her waspish self.

She gently drew aside the fabric, revealing what lay behind.

Weston reeled back.

Within the dark corner, mounted on draped trestles, rested a simple coffin. It contained the body of Isaac Gulliver. His face stared out from the far end, white and ghastly.

"You see now, sir." Mrs Gulliver turned to Weston. There was no spite in her eyes. "My husband had just passed away last night, when you called," she drew the curtain back, " and I wished the time to myself to grieve."

Mr Weston swallowed.

He was not an unkind man. No, he would not have enjoyed seeing Gulliver hanged. But the fates had been unkind to him, hadn't they? Just a little justice would not have gone amiss. Even now the man had beaten him. Even in death.

He collected the dragoon at the front step and left the house, passing the stables where black cloths were being fitted to a carriages wheels, and set his course for Poole. The warrant was of little use to him now. But, he cheered himself, with Gulliver gone, his life would be easier. Yes, he told himself, spurring his horse to a trot, life would be much easier indeed.

From an upper window of the house Mrs Gulliver watched the two men ride off. She followed their progress between the great oaks that flanked the lane, until they disappeared from view onto the Poole road.

Satisfied that they were gone, she descended the stair and, drawing back the curtain, turned into the darkened alcove.

She stroked the face within.

White powder brushed off onto the pillow beneath, and the gimlet eyes of the corpse snapped open like traps.

The story of Gulliver feigning death to escape a warrant is part of our rich folklore, and the legends, which cannot be discounted, tell of the coffin being interred carrying nothing but rocks to give it authenticity.

The location of the grave has been lost, but, folklore or not, it is a story worthy of the wiles of our Mr Isaac Gulliver.

Model of a smuggling lugger, Poole Museum.

Pug's Hole, now a 4.2 acre woodland site, accessed from Rothesay Road, Bournemouth.

This scale model of a fast trading vessel is by family tradition believed to be of one of Gulliver's ships. The model belongs to Mrs. Mary Lawton, niece to Mr and Mrs Sam Walker, direct descendents of Isaac Gulliver.

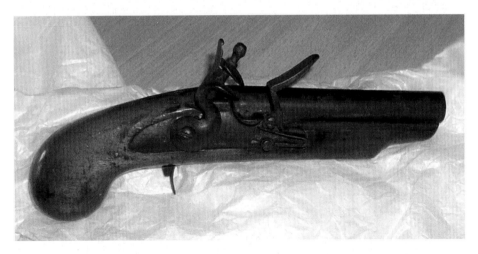

Isaac Gulliver's pistol, Russell- Cotes Museum, Bournemouth.

Howe Lodge, Brook Road, Kinson. This photograph is believed to have been taken before the turn of the 20th century.

A Lost Heritage

Gulliver owned several houses in Kinson but his headquarter is generally believed to have been Howe Lodge, a grand Georgian building, created in the 18th century, and most likely built for him. It was constructed out of Purbeck Stone and red brick, the latter probably coming from the brick-kilns to the west of the Congregational Chapel, which stands around 350 yards across what used to be meadows to the south.

The house was long and although rising to two stories, was not a tall building. It could be described as being built in three sections. The central section was the highest part, from which protruded a square castellated porch. Conclave hoods, probably clad in lead or copper, extended from the porch to the extent of this central section. There were three windows to the first floor of this part of the house, the middle one being of elegant Georgian proportions, larger than the others, and central to the porch roof.

The tiled roof above rose steeply, creating a flat roofed area around the massive central chimneystack. If this area were accessible from inside the house, it would have made a fine look-out post.

This photograph, taken at the porch of Howe Lodge, is believed to date back to the 1890's. The Reverend Arnold Mortimer Sharp MA of St Andrew's Church, Kinson, moved into Howe Lodge around 1891.

To the east and west of this central part were the two wings. Both similar in style, they each possessed two tall Georgian windows, the heads of which appeared to be level with the top of the central porch. The wall continued above, terminating in heavy castellation.

The message sent by this feature said much about the brazen nature of the owner.

The only other window to the front elevation of the two wings was one small dormer - which was a later addition - on the east roof. Both wings had chimneystacks on their end gables, the largest by far being the Western stack, as it served the kitchen below.

Beneath the house was a brick and purbeck stone cellar, which ran the length of the building and beyond.

The house was probably built on the foundations of an ancient defended farmhouse, born out by the fact that its stable block was Elizabethan and predated Howe Lodge by several hundred years. Other factors point to evidence of the nature of the earlier residence, and probably the reason of its attraction to a man like Gulliver.

Early maps of Howe Lodge show its northern perimeter boundary circling in an egg shaped arc around it, starting at Brook Road in the West and finally touching Brook Road again in the East.

This perimeter was defended against the outside world by means of a ditch or steep sided ha-Ha, like a moat, running its entire length, the purpose of which was to keep animals out. On the boundary itself is thought to have stood a ten foot high, thatched cob wall.

Along the length of the wall were support buttresses. On the outside these were smooth, whilst those on the inside of the wall had been stepped, which would allow you to climb up to see over the top.

In this wall was a gate of a very particular kind. It was hung with heavy leather hinges, instead of iron, which would allow its use silently, without fear of detection. It also had a crossbar mechanism, which would permit people to exit, but not get back in. The cross bar could also be reversed, enabling people to enter, but not to escape.

To the south of Brook Road was once a meadow and in the 1950s, before the housing development, there were signs of overgrown ditches.

These dents in the land were to be found in such a position as to indicate that they may well have mirrored the northern half of the ring. If this were the case, it is therefore possible that a defended moat once encircled a previous building, and would have helped to protect the inhabitants against unwelcome guests.

Howe Lodge itself had its fair share of surprises. On entering through the front door you found yourself in the grand central hallway. A winding staircase twisted up, disappearing around a corner on its way to the first floor, whilst a fine Georgian fireplace dominated the room. All appeared innocuous, but the wall of the fireplace held a secret.

Hidden within its paneling was a doorway to a passage. Within it were a series of rungs, like a ladder, leading about ten feet upwards to the entrance of a small room, no wider than four feet in width.

This room gave access through a trap door in its ceiling into the loft of the house. From here you had a choice, for if you wished to secretly visit your cellar, covertly call on a neighbour, or leave the grounds of the house, you could do so quite undetected from this starting point.

On the east and west gable ends of the building were two great thick walls, with the western wall at least being wide enough for a vertical tunnel to run down within it. This tunnel had rungs for descent through the very walls themselves, and took you secretly through both floors until finally dropping down into the capacious cellar. This subterranean room contained a well and, described in a report from the 1930s, it retained wooden racking for the storage of blunderbusses and other arms.

The western end, which could also be entered via a secret trap door under a carpet in one of the main rooms, extended beyond the foundations of the house above into another subterranean room. In the end wall of this was the entrance to the western tunnel. Its route, away from the house, took you in the direction of what is now known as Kinson Road.

There was a similar subterranean entrance at the other end of the building, through the eastern wall, although here the cellar did not extend further than the foundations of the house. This tunneled passage headed due east, on route towards a large nearby red brick house, built in the same period as Howe Lodge, and with similar architectural features.

When entered in the 1950's neither of these tunnels extended very far, with the eastern one attaining only 40ft before becoming blocked like the west tunnel with fallen rubble.

Woodlands, Brook Road, Kinson.

However, the red walled neighbouring property, which the tunnel headed towards, also held a secret. It was known by some locally, in the middle of the last century, as Red House, possibly because of its colour, although its name was Woodlands. But intriguingly it has also been suggested that the building may have been formerly known as Ridout's House.

Of course the name may simply be coincidental, but if indeed this was once our Mr Roger Ridout's house, then he and Gulliver would have made fine neighbours.

The view that the name is no more than coincidence becomes less convincing however, with the knowledge that there was also an entrance in the basement floor, facing in the direction of Howe Lodge. Now, little imagination is needed to make assumptions on the characters of the owners of these two houses. But that was not all, as from this basement, another passage is thought to have run on yet again, heading still further east towards what is now known as The Thatched House Inn.

Unfortunately, if there were a cellar in this charming period Inn it does not exist today, and of a secret entrance there appears to be no trace. Neither is there any sign of the tunnel which reputedly ran from it, carrying on its journey down the hill towards the nearby thatched Primrose Cottages.

The Thatched House Inn, East Howe Lane, Kinson.

The cottages and the Inn, which still retain attractive period windows, remain today, but Woodlands and Howe lodge have been destroyed.

Of Woodlands there is no sign, as the foundations are buried under a block of flats. But remarkably there are still some remains of Gulliver's House.

The fine Howe Lodge, like countless other period buildings which formed such a rich part of our island heritage, fell victim in the post war 1950s to the clamour of modernization.

However, in the case of Howe Lodge, although indeed a block of flats was built in part of the garden they were actually constructed well clear of the house. Tragically, Howe Lodge's crime was that it stood in the path of a proposed new service road scheme and in April 1958 it was demolished by the Corporation.

Primrose Cottages, East Howe Lane, Kinson.

This was a classic move, and quite breathtaking. The planned road as shown on the Council's drawings, was never built. But the Corporation, charged with the duty of preserving our culture, had removed forever a part of Kinson's rich ancient history, because it was an obstacle to their plans.

Site of Howe Lodge.

On visiting the site today one can still see the place where the Lodge once stood. With Brook Road to your back, the flats stand at an angle on the western segment of the old garden, whilst along their western boundary fence a tarmac road curves to the right into a cul-de-sac of housing. Between these two developments is a grassy patch, which opens out remarkably into what is left of Gulliver's garden.

The ghost of Howe Lodge stands in this entrance, with its West Wing brushing the boundary fence of the flats. Walk through into the garden area and you cross rubble. Fire glazed bricks and Purbeck stone, still stare out of the ground. Here, you can even today get a flavour of the place as although the house is gone, a few of the great trees in the planted avenue which struck north from the house to the boundary of its large garden, are still living.

They stand now as a proud sentinel to the past, lining the footpath which runs between them. At its end is a gateway, leading through to a green, tree lined sweep of land behind, known locally as Cuckoo Woods.

Footpath leading from the former Howe Lodge Garden.

By the late 1980s, although Howe Lodge had been long gone, it continued to intrigue, and gave up yet another pointer to its shady past. Whilst excavations were being carried out on the site, the archaeologists keeping a watching brief came across buried piles of old French brandy bottles. They were of 18th and 19th century origin, identified by their applied lips and the moulders' stamps.

Along with the bottles was unearthed some fine pottery, which was also of French derivation. But the interest really is in the bottles. They were identified as dating from Gulliver's period, and there were more than just a few. They had been stashed under the ground, concealed for centuries in their hiding place, not in mere dozens or even in hundreds, but in thousands.

Woodlands, however, had already revealed a far darker secret.

In 1951, not that many years after its use during World War Two as a billet for American servicemen, workmen, whilst digging a new footpath in the grounds, found a grisly reminder of the past.

They had unearthed a human skull. Tree roots were growing through it as it lay buried several feet under the surface. And as if that were not grim enough, this skull was quite out of the ordinary and could well be described as the thing of nightmares.

It was the skull of a male, of less than average size, and it had been impaled. Pierced through the top of its crown by a pointed iron spike. This gruesome rusted bar, lodged firmly within the unfortunate victim's head, still protruded eight inches skywards from the bone.

An officer of the Bournemouth Police, investigating the site and the find, told the Bournemouth Echo that in his opinion, *"It looks as if this was done before crime became crime as we know it."*

So that was that then.

It would be interesting however to know from just what period this relic belonged, and also the view of the incumbent Coroner. But, if there were any detailed records, their conclusions may never be known, as the relevant Coroner's records for that period cannot be found, and are considered, quite amazingly, to have been lost.

Another house in Kinson, known as Kinson House, also has strong connections to Gulliver. This house, thought to have been part of Gulliver's property empire, stood beside the present day Wimborne Road, just a short distance from the Royal Oak Inn. Sybil Thorndike, 1882 – 1976, and her brother Russell, 1885 – 1972, spent holidays at the house when they were children, staying with the then owners Lt. Colonel Godfrey Russell and his wife, Ada Augusta. Ada Augusta was the great granddaughter of Isaac Gulliver.

Sybil Thorndike was later to become a Dame, indeed the grand dame of British theatre, and one of the finest stage performers of the 20th century, whilst her brother Russell, who also became an actor, was perhaps better known as the creator of the 'Doctor Syn' novels. The lead character is a clergyman by day and a Romney Marsh Smuggler by night. Three films have been made based upon the characters, and in 1923 the original novel was put on as a stage play at the Strand Theatre in London, with Russell Thorndike himself as the lead.

The Romney Marshes are a long way from Kinson, but it is tempting to speculate that the young Russell Thorndike, whilst staying in Isaac Gulliver's great granddaughters house, would have gained at least some of his inspiration from tales of Kinson smugglers, and from the wild sweep of untamed heath-land which at that time still encircled the village.

MURDER AT

KINSON ?

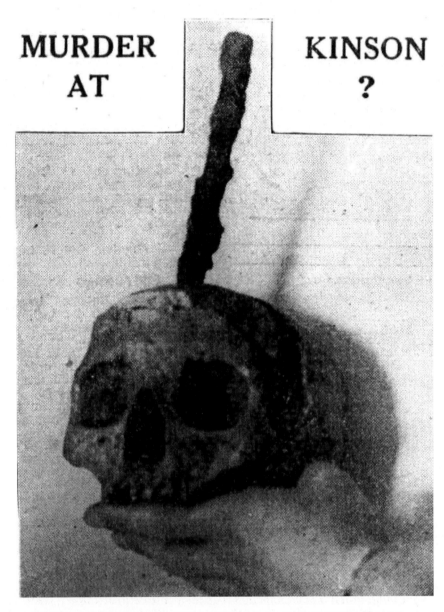

The mysterious skull found buried in the grounds of 'Woodlands',
Brook Road, Kinson. Picture reproduced by kind permission of the
Bournemouth Daily Echo.

Tobacco, and the Hidden Man

Across the water meadows from Wimborne Minster the land rises into the undulating and beautiful countryside surrounding the winding village of Corfe Mullen. Here, at Lamb's Green on the first rise into the village, resides a grand ancient farmhouse, known by local historians to be yet another property that once belonged to our master smuggler.

The house sits on the corner between Wimborne Road and Candy's Lane, and is a landmark on this eastern end of the village. It is an extraordinary building, and due to its construction and reputed ownership, legends abound concerning secret underground tunnels, going who knows where.

At first glance the house is difficult to date, but closer inspection reveals that the main body of the building and its south wing are of Georgian construction, possibly early 1800s, and are an addition to an earlier single story cob cottage. This cottage, which was given a second floor and now forms the north wing, may well date back to the 16th century.

It is the central Georgian block, however, which gives the building its character and its name, Highe House. For here the house rises to three stories, towering over the two side wings. This enables the top floor to possess windows which give an excellent view over the surrounding countryside, making it in fact quite perfect for Isaac Gulliver's purposes.

Highe House, Corfe Mullen in 1918. The house at the time belonged to the Tovey family. When this photograph was taken the central 3 storey Georgian section remained un-rendered and there was a glass building attached to the coach-house. Note the narrowness of the Wimborne Road, which appears to be little more than a lane.

Even today it still makes an ideal look out point, especially toward Wimborne, where the twin towers of the great Minster Church can be seen quite clearly, surrounded by the clay tiled rooftops of the ancient market town. And, perhaps more importantly, the high windows give a good view of the only road across the water meadows, along which the town's red coated Dragoons would have ridden when out on patrol.

The south wing of the house was once the original coach-house. It had at one time been used as a gallery by the artist Philip Marchington when he and his wife Kathleen were the owners of Highe House, but was extended and converted into living accommodation in the late seventies.

When the new foundations were being excavated the builders unearthed a pit full of broken clay pipes. The explanation offered at the time was that they

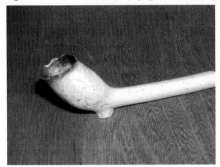

may have been manufactured on the site. Recent investigation however has found that many of the pipes showed clear signs of having been used, and some were even found embedded in the earth floor of the coach-house itself. This would suggest that the building could once have been a meeting place.

Two great seashells were also found amongst the pipes; they survive today along with a single pipe.

Clay pipe from excavation.

The old coach-house, before conversion.

Highe House.

In 1979, after the building and alteration work to the former coach-house had been completed, it became independent from the main building.

However much had become separated long before this, indeed in the 1950s and 60s a good deal of the land, which once stretched extensively south towards Corfe Halt Close and back as far as the railway line, had already come under new ownership.

Inside today, Highe House is the pleasant family home of John and Caite Coupe, their two sons Jack and Thomas, and the family cats. It has a warmth and character that few newer properties possess, and a friendly atmosphere. In fact, John and Caite speculate, it is almost as though the house has a mind of its own. Implausible you may think, but sometimes some things do just leave you wondering.

Launching into a sensitive and careful programme of maintenance, almost a decade ago, the pair have found that the house appears uncannily to help to look after itself.

Very early one morning, John had left the house for work. It was October 2000, the year of the floods, and it was raining. Caite watched his tail lights disappear, closed and locked the heavy back door after him, went through into the house, and back up to bed. Thirty minutes later a loud crashing noise came from the kitchen below, bringing her back down and into the room. Inexplicably the back door had blown open to crash against the wall. She closed and secured it again, and turned to see rainwater, built up by the torrential rain outside, seeping in fast under the kitchen door on the other side of the room. The water was rising fast and if Caite had not been there, right then, to scoop it up - she filled seven ten-litre buckets - the water would have flowed in and down the step to flood the living room carpet.

Caite was certain that she had locked the heavy door before going up, and it felt as though it were more than a twist of fate that she had been brought back down into the kitchen again at exactly the right time to avoid a flood.

Maybe this was an uncanny coincidence, or maybe not; like the careful choosing of a colour for the kitchen wall, which after stripping back the onion skins of wallpaper, exactly matched the original shade found beneath.

However, this was not the only surprise to be found in the kitchen. During renovation work to the floor a huge round tablet of purbeck stone was unearthed, underneath which was hidden a brick walled well. This well is in good working order and even today crystal clear water glints up from the bottom of its 5 metre shaft.

The well in the kitchen.

The stone well cover.

The house has long been rumoured to be haunted, indeed when John and Caite bought the property, the previous owners Philip and Kathleen made no secret of the stories, having themselves witnessed the sound of footsteps on the stairs and in the upper rooms. However, nothing began to manifest itself until about a month after the new owners had moved in. That was when John's mother came to stay the night. The next morning John was taken to task.

If he really needed to take up smoking strong pipe or cigar tobacco, he was to do it elsewhere and not whilst wandering about in the corridor outside his mothers room.

Needless to say that John, of course, does not smoke a pipe or cigars.

Years before non-smokers Philip and Kathleen, during their early days at the house, had also witnessed this phenomenon, when at that time the smoker visited them for several days running. Strangely it was also only on the first floor, and in the same vicinity.

This part of the house, which is now two bedrooms, was originally one big room, possibly the main living room.

Since John and Caite's more recent encounter, the smoker comes and goes.

Mysterious happenings you must agree, and you may ask yourself this: if a ghost really exists within the walls of Highe House, just who might it be? And who would feel the need to visit the upper rooms?

Could it be Isaac Gulliver watching out for the Revenue? Or has he got a lantern at the window, a lighthouse beam for his White Wigs to follow on a black night as they cross the misty water meadows, a shadowy strung out line of men, tubs on shoulders, on yet another audacious run.

In the not too distant past however, Highe House is known to have given up a few of its secrets.

There is a legend that a cache of weapons, including pistols, is said to have been discovered in one of the chimneys.

An exciting find and one that may be true - but it may have become blurred with another happening whilst the house was under the ownership of the Degnan family.

In the 1950's, Mr and Mrs Degnan moved to Highe House from their previous address, The Royal Oak, deep in the heart of Kinson. This of course had once been Gulliver's territory and The Royal Oak, prior to being rebuilt and run by the Degnans, was an ancient low whitewashed building, formerly known as The Traveler's Rest.

Mr Degnan was a builder by trade, and it is his hand that we have to thank for the distinctive green roof tiles that make Highe House the landmark we see today.

After moving to the property, Degnan became a prolific builder, constructing new properties throughout the area. And it was while he was working on one of his sites that he made a very interesting discovery, which he transported home.

Pistols; once at Highe House, Corfe Mullen.

His find had been a pair of pistols. And so it transpires that Highe House did possess a cache of weapons, but they had been found elsewhere. That elsewhere being in Northborne or Ensbury, both areas, coincidentally, which are right next-door to Kinson.

The weapons postdate Gulliver by many years however. One appears to be a German First World War flare pistol, and the other a more delicate pin fire revolver, possibly of 1860's Belgian origin.

Another find by Mr Degnan, however, was more intriguing, as it was definitely made inside Highe House itself. It was a painting - an oil painting on canvas, of a bearded man, of shrewd appearance, wearing a black hat. The unframed portrait, scarred by the years, had allegedly been hidden in a cavity beneath the front door step. Was this a secret hiding place for valuables? Had the painting been forgotten? And mysteriously, just who was the owner of the astute face?

We will probably never know for sure, but one thing is certain. Everyone that had passed into the hallway, would have stepped over the piercing gaze, hidden and waiting, below the threshold of Highe House.

The hidden man, Highe House, Corfe Mullen.

A Strange Affair and the Growth of a Bank

In the October of 1796, Isaac and Elizabeth's daughter Ann, of Long Critchell, married Edmund Wagg, of Burton House near Christchurch. The wedding took place at Frome in Somerset. She was twenty-three years old, her husband was two years her junior. However their marriage was soon to fail, and indeed was the start of an extraordinary and tragic chain of events.

In fact the marriage appears to have lasted for just nine months, as by June of the following year, Ann had found it necessary to leave the matrimonial home.

We are not privy to know just exactly why the union failed, but that it was an acrimonious parting was made quite clear by the thwarted husbands public proclamation. She had not left home unassisted nor empty handed, and Wagg felt it appropriate to issue a public notice to the effect.

He accused her of not only taking with her all his plate and linen, but also of leaving in the company of another, of elopement with another man, with her brother, Isaac Gulliver junior.

We can read what we like into this strange affair, but it was soon to take another twist of a sadder and ultimately more puzzling nature. In November 1798, within two years of the break up, Ann's brother, Isaac, died at the age of 24.

It is believed that the illness was pneumonia, caused by sleeping on a damp mattress. Whatever the reason for his demise, losing a son so young would have been a great tragedy for the Gulliver family. However it seems that they were not the only ones to grieve at young Isaac's passing.

On the inner wall of the west tower, the Baptistery, in the great Minster Church Of St Cuthberga in the market town of Wimborne, is mounted a memorial. It is positioned high up, just below and to the right of the beautiful Astronomical Clock, and bares a curious epitaph; or two, to be precise.

The sad story is carved dark into its cold stone face.

Above. The memorial to Edmund Wagg and Isaac Gulliver's son, in the Baptistery, Wimborne Minster.

Firstly it is to the memory of Isaac Gulliver, of Long Critchell, but it also bears the name of his brother-in-law, Edmund Wagg, of Burton. Edmund, it transpires, died just five months after Isaac, also aged just twenty-four, and left in his Will an earnest request.

His wish was that he be interred in the same vault as the other man.

The casing on the memorial is ornate and two cherub faces stare out from below the written word.

 Ann, released from her vows, was not however forgotten in Wagg's Will, in which she was bequeathed all the mansion houses, freehold, leasehold, and copyhold lands, tenements and hereditaments in her former husband's possession. Presumably now a wealthy young widow in her own right, Ann went on to marry Andrew Crawford of Blandford Forum, Doctor Of Physic, with whom, by accounts, she led a happy life.

Thickthorne Farm.

The memorial to the two young men in the above account, confirms that in 1798 Isaac Gulliver was 'of Long Crichel'. He was also listed as being resident there at the time of his daughter's marriage, and again at the time when he first began writing his lengthy and detailed Will. Documents of the Crichel Estate, tell us that it was in the year of 1793 that Charles Sturt Esquire, leased Gulliver Long Crichel North East Farm and Thickthorne Farm for the period of 14 years, describing Gulliver at that time as being a merchant of West Moors.

Thickthorne Farm stands to this day, and at the time would have been in an ideal position for Gulliver's business. The building, which possesses a substantial cellar, stands close to the main A354 Blandford to Salisbury road on the junction of Millers Lane, a short distance from Chettle, and, unsurprisingly, just over two miles south west of The Kings Head in Thorney Down.

Elizabeth Fryer nee Gulliver, 1770 – 1839, Isaac Gulliver's eldest daughter.

Thought to be Ann Crawford nee Gulliver 1773 – 1832, Isaac Gulliver's second daughter.

Isaac Gulliver, 1774 – 1798, son of Isaac Gulliver. An oil painting hangs in Mirehouse, Keswick.

Edmund Wagg, 1774 – 1799, husband of Gulliver's second daughter, Ann.

These two untitled miniatures may well be of the young William Fryer and Elizabeth Gulliver.

Another image of Ann Gulliver, who after the death of her husband Edmund Wagg, married Dr Crawford of Blandford.

William Fryer, 1770 – 1834, husband of Gulliver's eldest daughter, Elizabeth.

Gulliver's eldest daughter Elizabeth, who had been born in 1770, married William Fryer of Lytchet House near Poole, and they were to have six sons and one daughter.

Fryer was a wealthy banker and a man of business. John Druitt of Wimborne, born 1816, writes in his memoir that before Druitt's time Fryer the banker of Wimborne had a drapers business and was engaged in the Poole shipping trade. Druitt also gives us a rare written description of one of the Gulliver family, when he describes Elizabeth, in his manuscript, as *a very fine and handsome woman.*

Isaac Gulliver was a rich man by the time of this marriage and as he was known to be a "person of great speculating genius", one can imagine him investing well in his daughter's new partnership.

Apart from the family's other interests, it is believed that this Gulliver-Fryer union also had an investment in as many as ten local Inns.

In 1823, at the age of 53, Elizabeth saw her daughter Ann (Gulliver's granddaughter) married to Edward Castleman. This was another fortunate match, as Castleman was not only a steward, but like his father-in-law he was also a local banker.

After Anne Fryer and Edward Castleman's marriage came the union of the two banks, which became known as the Fryer and Castleman Bank.

Anne Castleman, nee Fryer,
1800 – 1883, Gulliver's granddaughter.

Edward Castleman,
1800 - 1861.

Initially the newly-weds took up residence in what is now called 'The Olive Branch' in East Borough, formerly Crooked Borough, Wimborne. This attractive period house was then owned by the Gulliver Fryer family. Later the couple moved across Prior's Walk to the grander and more contemporary Allendale House, which was more fitting for people of their wealth. They moved again to Chettle House, which is to the east of Blandford Forum. This house was initially put up for sale in 1825, and the Castlemans paid the deposit. But there was a dispute as to the title, and it was not until 1846 that the family finally took possession of the house and parish.

The Fryer and Castleman Bank later became Fryer Andrews and Company, which by 1841 was incorporated with The National Provincial Bank of England. A business which made it clear in a Bank Review of the 1950s, that it was well aware of its distant connections with the romantic character of Isaac Gulliver.

Finally, in 1968 the bank announced their decision to merge with the Westminster Bank, and the year of 1970 saw the creation of The National Westminster Bank, now known as NatWest.

And so we see Isaac Gulliver's smuggling legacy living on and touching our lives today. For it is through his outstanding qualities of judgement and enterprise, and subsequent wealth, that his name is bound up in the fledgling past of a small local bank - a bank which has developed over the centuries into one of the greatest banks of the modern world.

Bournemouth became developed during Gulliver's granddaughter Ann Castleman's lifetime, and it was whilst the family owned 11, Westover Villas, which overlooked the Bourne Stream, that she is credited to have been instrumental in the design of Bournemouth's beautiful gardens.

SACRED TO THE MEMORY OF
WILLIAM FRYER ESQ.
of WIMBORNE MINSTER AND LYTCHET, DORSET,
BANKER.
DIED MARCH 1834, AGED 64 YEARS.
ALSO ELIZABETH. HIS WIFE,
DAUGHTER OF ISAAC GULLIVER ESQ.
OF WEST MOORS, DORSET,
DIED 1839 AGED 69 YEARS

The Fryer Monument, St. Andrews Churchyard, Kinson.

The Olive Branch, 6 East Borough, Wimborne; former home to Ann, granddaughter of Isaac Gulliver, and her husband, William Castleman. The house is now a popular restaurant bar, with a garden oasis to the rear, stretching down to the river Allen.

Allendale House, Hanham Road, Wimborne. This house was built by the Castlemans in 1823 and became the home of Gulliver's granddaughter Ann and her husband William Castleman. The building is now the home of The East Dorset Heritage Trust, an environmental education charity.

Fireside Tales and a Show of Defiance

 Unsubstantiated legends regarding Isaac Gulliver have been passed down to us over the centuries. They may have once been based on factual events, been diluted, enhanced or romanticized, but they exist none-the-less, and are worth recounting here.

   One story tells of Isaac Gulliver being a well-known smuggler in Poole with a price on his head. At the time of the telling he is said to have been living in the village of Longham. Here we may decide to date the story, as Gulliver is said to have moved, in 1779, from the King's Head in Thorney Down, to the White Hart in Longham.

   From here, dressed as a shepherd and with a flock of sheep, he visited the nearby town of Wimborne, although we are not told for what reason. However, once in town he avoided the revenue men who were searching for him everywhere, by sitting around in the market square the whole day, undetected, and uncaught, due to his peasant's disguise.

The Corn Market, Wimborne Minster.

   At another time, Gulliver is said to have successfully traveled through Poole, hidden in a cask. There was a very high price being offered for his capture, but, by his unique method of transport, he once more outwitted and avoided 'the Revenue'.

   These snippets of stories are fun, but the next, written in the Poole Pilot, July 1st 1867, has more of the ring of truth about it.

It reports an eyewitness account of the events of one night in the year of 1800, on the shore of what one-day would become Bournemouth. In fact, we are informed, in the place where the pier now reaches out into Poole bay.

It was here that three luggers were seen by an 'old inhabitant'. They were heavily laden and manned by determined crews, busily running their cargo consisting of brandy, tobacco, silks and other valuables on to the waiting beach.

The size of the loads must have been considerable, as the witness goes on to recount that the line of smugglers transporting the contraband extended for a distance of two miles into the heath-land beyond the shore, whilst at the head of the procession rode the Old Chief mounted on a spirited charger – here, for 'Old Chief', read Isaac Gulliver.

The report tells us that this was such an audacious show of strength by Gulliver that the Revenue Officers, being no doubt greatly outnumbered, would have been powerless to interfere. Romantically, it also has Gulliver retiring after this last run, and spending the rest of his days on shore in the enjoyment of his vast fortune.

Interestingly the story also informs us that in 1800 there was only one solitary habitation in the whole vast area which is now Bournemouth, and even that was the home of a smuggler. It also refers to the Revenue Officers as 'Philistines' and 'Land-sharks'.

So, no love lost there then.

Bournemouth Gardens. Photograph courtesy of Bournemouth Tourism.

Portrait of a Smuggler

We are lucky to have at least one authentic portrait of Gulliver: a miniature by the respected artist Thomas Gosse. This was painted when Gulliver was an old man, and more detail of its commission comes later in this book. However, there are two other images worthy of note. The first one is the shrewd face found hidden in Highe House, and the second is a painting, thought to depict Gulliver, which once hung in the Tregonwell Arms in Bournemouth.

No provenance has yet been found for the Highe House portrait, interesting though it is, but the painting from the Tregonwell Arms was created by a known artist, Henry Perlee-Parker, 1795 -1873 and is of particular interest in our search for Isaac Gulliver.

This painting is thought to depict Gulliver on the cliffs of Bourne Mouth.

The painting, thought to have been called either 'Smugglers At Bourne Mouth' or 'Halt; Smugglers', hung in the Tregonwell Arms - said to be the first public house in Bournemouth - until its demolition in 1884. Hopefully it was removed prior to the building being pulled down, as its whereabouts now are unknown.

Its creator, Henry Perlee-Parker, painted many busy romantic images of the day, giving a wonderful snapshot of the time, its everyday working folk, and its fishermen and seagoing characters, including a portrait of the heroin Grace Darling.

Is this Gulliver sharing a joke, on the cliff-tops at Bournemouth?

The Bournemouth painting, 'Halt; Smugglers', is full of interest, with the central figure - surrounded by ten men in all manner of poses - thought to be none other than Isaac Gulliver himself. The powerful face of this character certainly bears a fair resemblance to that painted by Gosse when our smuggler was in old age.

The scene is highly romantic of course; the jolly smuggling gang appearing to have climbed to a high point with their booty, before stopping for food and drink. To the right, two more men, deep in conversation with the seascape behind, can be seen ascending the slope leading pack horses. Top left, stretching into the distance, we can see the Bournemouth cliffs dropping down towards the beach below.

Centre-stage Gulliver himself, knife in one hand, bread in the other, appears to be sharing a joke with a black African, who is sat behind him to his right, whilst just behind Gulliver and to his left, we see the head of a golden haired dog, watching meat being carved with interest.

If we take it that Henry Perlee-Parker - also known allegedly as Smuggler Parker, due to his choice of subject - painted a fair likeness, and that this is indeed Gulliver, then we may dare to assume that the other members of the gang could also have been faithfully depicted in Parker's picture. Therefore it is possible that we see in the painting not just Gulliver, but also the faces of some of his notorious associates, plus one dog.

But just how would Gulliver have looked in his prime? With modern technology and the painting by Gosse it is possible to try to get a glimpse of the younger man.

(a)   *(b)*

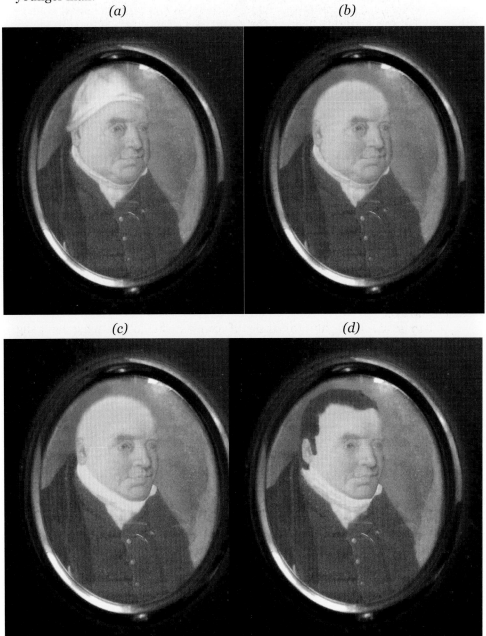

(c)   *(d)*

In figure (a) we see the portrait of Gulliver, painted by Gosse. Figure (b) shows the white cloth cap removed. In figure (c) we can see the jowls of the old man have been reduced, and the bags beneath the eyes smoothed slightly. Hair is then added and Figure (d) shows the result: no alteration has been made to Gulliver's eyes nose or mouth; they are the same as in the original picture.

The face of Isaac Gulliver
hidden beneath the years and the white cloth cap.

The Wimborne Resident

Gulliver appears to have remained resident at Long Critchell from the time of his lease of Thickthorne Farm and North East Farm in 1793 until the end of his lease in 1807. From there, in 1815, he moved back again to Kinson, and then in 1817, at the age of 72, he made his final move, taking up residence at number 45, West Borough, Wimborne; a town where he is thought to have owned a wine shop.

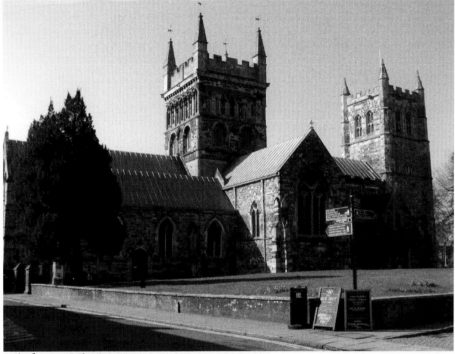

Wimborne Minster.

By this stage in his life, Isaac Gulliver had become a respected and honest citizen. So much so, in fact, that he was appointed to be one of the churchwardens at Wimborne's Minster Church of St Cuthberga.

What better progression for him to make. After all, through his association with St Andrew's in Kinson, his name had been linked with the Christian Church for many years. But not just for his smuggling activities.

Gulliver was a man of many parts. He may have been on the wrong side of the law, but he also had connections within the church. In 1794 he is mentioned in records as having sold the churchwardens of St Andrews a quantity of limestone for one shilling and sixpence. And he was also a trustee of the Weare charity at the church. This trust administered to the poor and needy from profits made on land donated by John Weare. The annual distribution was not great, but it was at least ten shillings, and in a world with no welfare state this was more than the poor would otherwise have received.

By this we can assume an insight into Gulliver's character, and an understanding as to why local folklore holds him in such high esteem. It may also go some way to explain why in a time when considerable rewards were offered for information, and in Gulliver's case they would be great indeed, that he appears never to have been betrayed.

By night, through his nocturnal activities, Isaac Gulliver bolstered the pittance of a wage that many suffered, whilst he also found the time - through the Weare charity - to assist those unable to help themselves.

His acceptance in a position of importance within the Church therefore, seems to be well deserved.

Gulliver's House, 45 West Borough, Wimborne.

It was while Gulliver and his wife Elizabeth were living in West Borough, that Thomas Gosse painted their portraits in miniature. The year was 1821. The backs of the miniatures reveal that Gulliver had passed his 76th birthday and Elizabeth her 80th. This indicates that the portraits were painted in the autumn of the year.

Gulliver's front door onto West Borough, Wimborne.

Gosse, who was traveling and taking commissions, was an accomplished artist. One of his larger creations entitled *Transplanting of the Bread Fruit Trees from Otaheite*, featuring William Bligh with the Tahitian King, now hangs in The Cook Museum in Whitby.

The miniatures, however, are far more modest affairs, depicting two model citizens in old age. But this does not mean that Gosse was unaware of the former nature of his sitters - there would be many a local no doubt willing to tell a tale or two over a tankard in a local tavern - or if indeed at the time of commission whether Isaac Gulliver, was not still plying his trade.

The sittings may well have been in the parlour of the house. A house, which, then as now, would give little away.

Our man may have been a churchwarden, but his home still carried the mark of his trade. This elegant Georgian building, whilst being large and comfortable, with an air of genteel respectability, made an ideal mask for the business of its residents and concealed within its walls, access to a covert room; a room large enough to hide a fortune in contraband. The room, quite hidden from view, exists between number 25 and its neighbour and is accessed via a hatch from the loft space of Gulliver's house, or from a hatch of the attic next door.

It can't be proved that the room was ever used for contraband, but nonetheless, it is typical Gulliver.

Old stories tell of tunnels running from this house as far as the Minster. These are made more mysterious by the fact that the Colourcraft shop, number 11 West Borough, a little way down the street, shows signs of bricked-up doors in its cellar. Also, right next door to number 11, evidence of what could have been a passage was unearthed once at The Old Tuck Shop. However, the only indication that there may have been an underground tunnel from number 25 is an intriguing brick arch at ground level on the outer wall. This feature is the tell tale sign that the house once possessed a cellar, but which is now filled in and inaccessible.

It is likely that the barn, now demolished, but once belonging to the house, was of a similar age, and here we may be able to date the property, as a brick found in the barn wall was heavily engraved with the year 1746, which was the year after Gulliver's birth. Towards the end of his life, it is reported that Gulliver's mode of transport through Wimborne was by bath chair, pushed by his man, John.

Isaac Gulliver esq.   Mrs Elizabeth Gulliver.

Isaac Gulliver died on Friday 13th September 1822 at the grand age of 77. He left behind a twelve thousand word Will, and an estate including farmland and properties throughout Dorset - many being in the area of Kinson - valued, then, at around sixty thousand pounds. In the early nineteenth century this was a vast fortune, and today his estate would be worth many millions of pounds. Isaac Gulliver was a very wealthy man indeed.

He was interred inside the Minster Church, a privileged place, and his grave-stone was set between the two churchwarden's seats, in the nave, also privileged, but perhaps there so they could keep a wary eye on him.

However, over the centuries, countless feet walking across his stone had begun to make his name unreadable, and so in the 1990s it was removed, and replaced with plain stones. It can now be seen on the inside wall of the west tower - the baptistery - opposite the memorial to his son.

The inscription is unassuming, almost humble, it simply announces his name, for all to see, bold and large, on the stone tablet on the wall;

the name of the man that brought the gentry fine wines and tobacco and their ladies the silk for their dresses;

the man who put food on the table of the poor farm worker;

the charismatic smuggler, who ruled his south coast empire with cunning and guile, and saw no man murdered under his reign;

the man of great speculating genius;

the greatest smuggler of all;

ISAAC GULLIVER ESQ.

Reverse side of Isaac Gulliver's miniature.

Reverse side of Elizabeth Gulliver's miniature.

Gulliver's House, 45 West Borough, Wimborne.

Bricked up openings in the cellar of Colourcraft, West Borough, Wimborne.

Colourcraft, 11 West Borough, Wimborne, Gulliver's House is at the end of the row.

A rough guide to Gulliver's Dorset

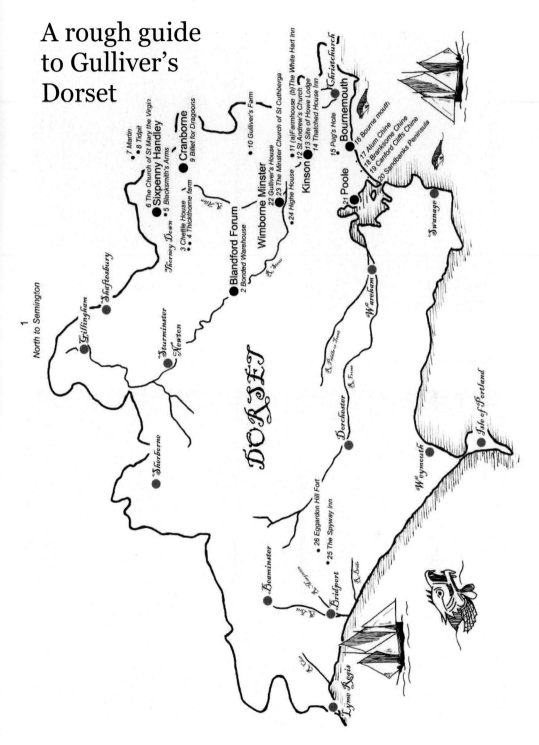

North to Semington

1

Shaftesbury

Gillingham

Sturminster Newton

Sherborne

Thorney Down

7 Martin
8 Tidpit
6 The Church of St Mary the Virgin
Sixpenny Handley
5 Blacksmith's Arms
3 Chettle House
4 Thickthorne farm
9 Billet for Dragoons

Cranborne

10 Gulliver's Farm

Blandford Forum
2 Bonded Warehouse

DORSET

Wimborne Minster
22 Gulliver's House
23 The Minster Church of St Cuthberga
24 Highe House

11 (a)Farmhouse (b)The White Hart Inn
13 Site of Howe Lodge
12 St Andrew's Church
14 Thatched House Inn
Kinson

15 Pug's Hole
16 Bourne mouth
Bournemouth
Christchurch

17 Alum Chine
18 Branksome Chine
19 Canford Cliffs Chine
20 Sandbanks Peninsula

21 Poole

Swanage

Wareham

R. Frome

Dorchester

Weymouth

Isle of Portland

26 Eggardon Hill Fort
25 The Spyway Inn

Beaminster

Bridport

Lyme Regis

Index to Map of Gulliver's Dorset.

1 To the village of Semington in Wiltshire; the birthplace of Isaac Gulliver, and location of St George's Churchyard, which contains Gulliver's father's grave. Semington is just over 40 miles north of Blandford Forum, on the A350, and 4 miles to the west of Trowbridge. The beautiful Kennet and Avon Canal flows under Semington Bridge. There are two locks here and access to the towpath on the northern bank.

2 Blandford Forum on the River Stour; scene, in the spring of 1788, of a raid on the bonded warehouse in White Cliff Mill Street, by heavily armed mounted smugglers. The town was rebuilt in 1731, after the second of two great fires - the first being in 1713. Two brothers, John and William Bastard, both distinguished architects, entrepreneurs and politicians, completed the work within thirty years. As a result, Blandford Forum is one of the best-preserved Georgian market towns in England. Beres Yard, off the market place, leads to the Blandford Forum Museum, which offers a fascinating insight into Blandford's past, including a scale model of the town during the second great fire. The barred doors from 'the bonded warehouse' that were broken open by the smuggling gang in 1788, now hang on the museum's gable end.

79 above. Weathervane in the garden of Gulliver's House, Wimborne.

3 Chettle House; in the village of Chettle, just under 7 miles east of Blandford, off the A354. This house, designed by Thomas Archer, was the home of the Chafin family from the reign of Elizabeth 1st until 1818. Gulliver's daughter, Elizabeth, and her husband William Castleman, took possession of the house and parish in 1846. William Beale's tomb can be found in the churchyard of nearby St Mary's Church.

4 Thickthorne Farm, is situated at Thickthorne Cross on the A354, a short distance past the turning to Chettle. In 1793, Gulliver, described as being a merchant of West Moors, leased Thickthorne Farm for a period of 14 years.

5 The former Blacksmith's Arms; now a private residence, on the A354, between Blandford Forum and Sixpenny Handley. Gulliver made this former Inn his headquarters after marrying Elizabeth Beale, the Innkeepers daughter. Shortly after Gulliver's arrival the inn changed its name to The King's Head.

6 The Church of St Mary the Virgin, Sixpenny Handley; setting for Gulliver's marriage to Elizabeth Beale on 5th October 1768. Sixpenny Handley, on the B3081, just over 11 miles east of Blandford Forum, lies in the heart of the picturesque and historic Cranborne Chase. This ancient settlement suffered a series of fires over the centuries until in 1892 it was virtually destroyed, and subsequently rebuilt. However, the 13th century church remains. The village derives its name from two medieval 'hundreds' Sexpena and Hanlega, which over the years has become abridged to the delightful Sixpenny Handley.

7 The ancient village of Martin; off the A354, 6.4 miles from Sixpenny Handley, leads to the staggered crossroads of Tidpit. Martin contains many picturesque cottages and farmhouses; some dating back to the 15th century.

8 Tidpit; crossroads on the old road from Poole, via Wimborne and Cranborne, to Salisbury. Tidpit, now a quiet staggered crossroads, was reputedly a notorious centre for the contraband trade. Here, beside Angel Lane, on the old main road to Salisbury once stood a malt-house, which may also be the site of The Angel Inn. Windmill hill - where old maps indicate the presence of a windmill - looks down on the crossroads, and the ancient milestones can still be seen along the lush banks of the narrow winding road.

9 Cranborne; Billet for the Dragoons overwhelmed by smugglers in Hook's Wood, Farnham; 4.1 miles from Tidpit, and just under 10 miles from Wimborne Minster. This charming red brick village, sitting astride the river Crane, gives its name to the former Royal Forest of Cranborne Chase.

10   Gulliver's Farm; on the B3072 at West Moors, on the route north to Cranborne from the beach-heads. This historic building is 9.5 miles south of Cranborne and 5 miles from Kinson.

11 (a) The ancient Hillamsland Farmhouse at Dudsbury - another of Gulliver's residences - sits beside the B3073 at the entrance to Dudsbury Golf Club. (b) The delightful White Hart Inn is under I mile away to the west on the A348 at Longham, Gulliver appears to have moved here in 1779 from the notorious King's Head Inn, at Thorney Down. Both these locations are approximately 3 miles from West Moors, and 2.5 miles from Kinson to the south.

12   St Andrew's Church, Millham's Road, off the A341, Wimborne Road, Kinson, 2.5 miles from Dudsbury. This beautiful ancient church is set in stunning countryside, just to the southwest of Kinson Splash. In the graveyard can be found the gravestone of the unfortunate Robert Trottman. Kinson is 6 miles from Wimborne Minster to the north west, and 5 miles from Bournemouth Pier. (Bournemouth Pier is where the Bourne Stream reaches the shore of Poole Bay; this was formerly known as Bourne mouth, and identified as a fair landing place.)

13 The site of Howe Lodge, Brook Road, Kinson. There is nothing to show of this 'house of secrets' today. However a few great trees and a green space, which was once the garden, still remain. Although lined by modern housing, the narrow undulating Brook road, shaded by its ancient trees, still gives a flavour of Kinson's rural past.

14 The Thatched House Inn, East Howe Lane. This delightful 17th century thatched building is thought to have been linked by a subterranean tunnel to Howe Lodge, and even to St Andrew's Church. Formerly part of the Lady Wimborne Estate, the cottage was once owned by Thomas Stone and known as Stonehill Cottage. Stone also at one time is thought to have owned Howe Lodge. Down the hill and on the opposite side of the road can be seen the thatched Primrose cottages. These are also rumoured to have been served by mysterious underground passageways.

15 Pug's Hole, Bournemouth; thought to have been named after a smuggler who hid contraband goods here when the area was predominantly heathland. Pug's Hole is now a small 4.2 hectare woodland site accessed from Rothesay Road. This verdant oasis is 2 miles from Bournemouth Pier (Bourne Mouth).

16 Bourne Mouth; Where one old inhabitant witnessed the unloading of contraband onto the beach, then watched a line of smugglers, stretching two miles in length, convey the goods inland. At the head rode the formidable figure of Isaac Gulliver. Today a pleasant walk or bike ride exists along the

Bourne Valley Greenway which begins where the Bourne Stream reaches the pier and heads north in a similar direction to that taken by the smugglers. This route takes the walker through Bournemouth's beautiful gardens to Coy Pond, which lies to the west of Pug's Hole, and onwards across Talbot Heath to Canford Heath beyond.

17, 18, 19 Alum, Branksome, and Canford Cliffs Chines; superb safe and sandy beaches, with promenades and woodland walks behind. Here the fine golden sands slope gradually with gentle shelving, making them an excellent choice for families with small children. In days gone by these outstanding beaches were the scenes of clandestine 'landings' and great activity. One of them, probably Canford Cliffs Chine, once known as Bitman's Chine, ran red with blood and slaughter on 24th March 1765.

20 Sandbanks Peninsula; approximately 2.5 miles from Canford Cliffs chine. This highly sought after and densely built up area of land was once the desolate setting for North Haven House. It was in this lonely spot that a jury of smugglers pronounced their lawful verdict on the death of one of their number.

21 Poole Museum, situated at the top of Poole High Street, off the Quay; just under 5 miles from Sandbanks. Here the story of Poole and its people are told. It is the perfect setting to display Poole's past and amongst the atmospheric displays is a scale model of a smuggling lugger.

22 Gulliver's House, West Borough, Wimborne Minster; Gulliver lived here from at least 1817 until 1822. It was here that he and Elizabeth, his wife, had their portraits painted in miniature, by Thomas Gosse. The charmingly picturesque town of Wimborne Minster is approximately 7.5 miles from Poole to the south, and around 6 miles from Kinson, to the east.

23 The Minster Church of St Cuthberga; founded AD 705. This magnificent twin-towered Church is home to many fascinating historical treasures including a unique chained library, established in the 17th century, a glorious 14th century astronomical clock, and the famous Quarterjack, a brightly coloured grenadier, who strikes the quarters every hour. Isaac Gulliver is buried within the church. His gravestone can be seen on the wall of the Baptistery, opposite the memorial to his son and Edmund Wagg.

24 Highe House, Corfe Mullen; 1.5 miles, across the water meadows to the south west of Wimborne Minster. This historic Georgian 3 storey farmhouse, once the possession of Isaac Gulliver, stands sentinel on the corner of Candy's Lane and Wimborne Road.

25 The Spyway Inn, Spyway; to the north of Askerswell, off the A35, approx 34.5 miles west of Wimborne Minster. This reputedly smugglers haunt sits beside the narrow winding lane, leading up to Eggardon Hill Fort.

26 Eggardon Hill Fort, approximately 36 miles from Wimborne Minster; an ancient iron-age hill-fort, once owned by Isaac Gulliver. This high place commands magnificent views across the countryside to the sea beyond, and provides a clearly visible landmark from the sea.

Bibliography

V. J. Adams, *Notes On Isaac Gulliver The Smuggler*
Bournemouth Library, *Biographical notes*
Roger Guttridge, *Dorset Smugglers*
Rodney Haskell, *Notes on Kinson and Dorset's most famous uncrowned king of smuggling.*
H. F. V. Johnstone, *Gulliver, Isaac 1745-1830*
S. J. Lands, *Old Kinson*
A. J. Miller, *Baccy Rum and Tea from Poole*
Priest House Museum, *The Druitt Papers*
Geoffrey Morley, *Smuggling in Hampshire and Dorset 1700-1850*
E. Russell Oakley, *The Smugglers of Christchurch, Bourneheath and The New Forest*
Joan M. Pitts and Wyn Watts, *Through a Georgian Window*
Bernard C. Short, *Smuggling in Poole Bournemouth and Neighbourhood*
David S. Young, *The story of Bournemouth*

Acknowledgements

My grateful thanks goes to all who have made this book possible through their kind assistance with my research. I have been helped and guided on numerous occasions by those that I have met in my search throughout the County. Others have assisted most generously by phone and by mail; all have been invaluable and have never ceased to inspire me with their generosity and enthusiasm for the subject.

Blandford Forum Museum Trust; E.T.C. Bourke, Chettle Estate; Peter and Fiona Bourke, Chettle Estate; Bournemouth Library; Bournemouth Natural Science Society; Michael Stead, Conservation Team, Bournemouth Borough Council; Scott Harrison, The Bournemouth Daily Echo, Archive Department; Dorset County Museum, Dorchester; Dorset History Centre, Dorchester; Beate and Dave Braban, Dudsbury Golf Club; The Cook Museum Whitby; John and Caite Coupe, Highe House, Corfe Mullen; Ann Degnan, Parkstone; James Fryer-Spedding; Iain Giles, Martin; Rodney Haskell, Kinson; The Curator, Captain W. A. Henshall, The Regimental Museum of the Royal Dragoon Guards, York; Colin Jones JP, Branksome; Robert and Mary Lawton; Doug and Olive Light, Gulliver's House, Wimborne; Lynne and Tony, and the staff and customers of the Thatched House Inn, Kinson; Kathlene Marchington, Corfe Mullen; Molly Old, Branksome; Christine Oliver, Wimborne Minster; Poole Central Library; Poole Museum; The Priest House Museum Trust, Wimborne; Russell-Cotes Art Gallery and Museum, Bournemouth; Sheriff S. Payne, The Coroner's Court, Bournemouth; J. Sansom; Will Sterling M A; Hazel and Martin Thorby, West Moors; Ken Waddon, The Old Thorney Down; Mike Winchester, Colourcraft, Wimborne; Ken Woodvine, Martin; and grateful thanks for the encouragement and forbearance of Alison Aquilina, Doreen Cory, Suzanne Gillespie, Fiona Knight, and Judy Monckton.

Many of the images are from the authors own collection, however, the following have kindly made illustrations available for inclusion within this book: I. Giles; C. Jones; Captain W. A. Henshall; R. and M. Lawton; H. and M. Thorby; The Bournemouth Daily Echo; K. Marchington; R. Haskell; and by kind permission of the Chettle Estate;
Every effort has been made to trace copyright holders of photographs used in this book and I apologize for any accidental offence that may have been caused in cases where an owner was unable to be traced.

Jacket: photocomposite by M. Angel, based on a photograph by Paul Angel.